GRADE

4



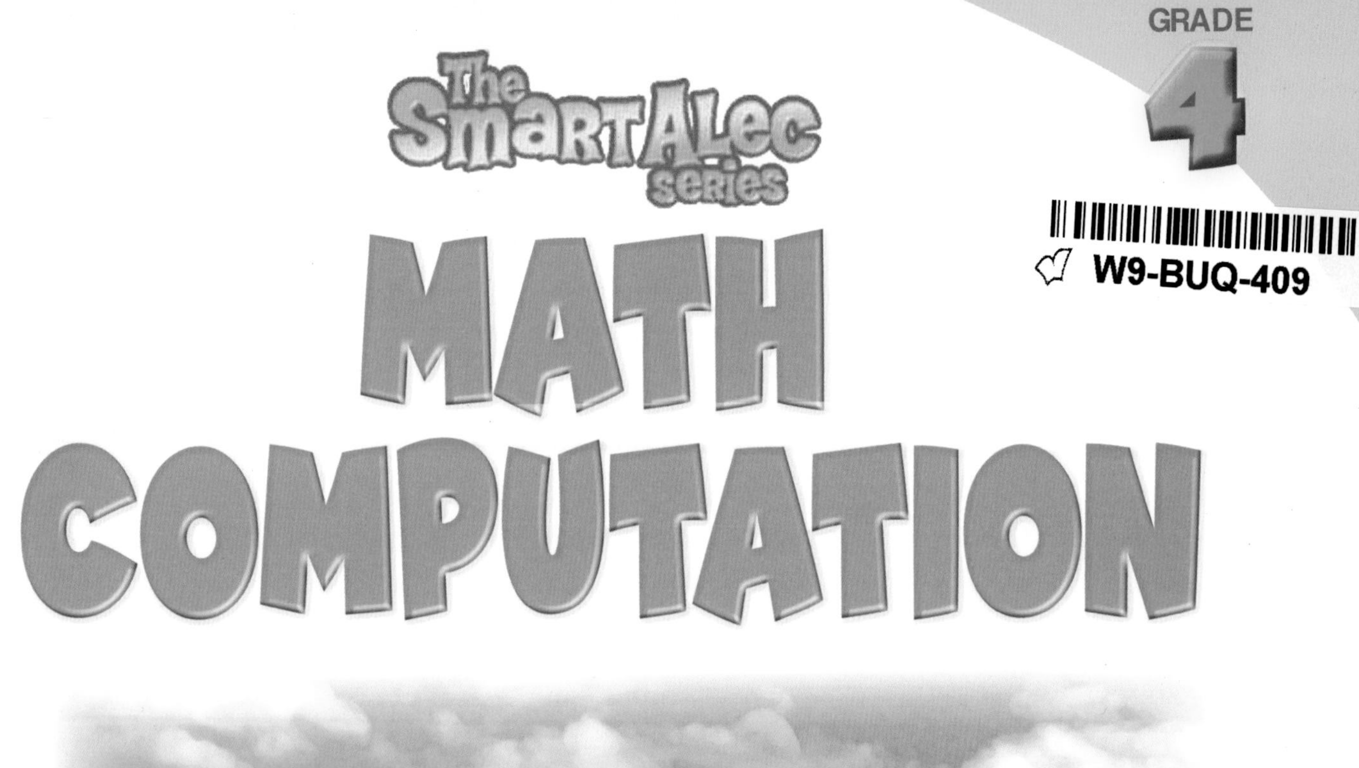

edgeucational
publishing

# MAKE IT FUN!

Dear Parent/Caregiver,

Welcome! This workbook is designed in such a way that your child can move through them on his or her own. In addition, there are other important and fun ways in which you can engage your child, thereby making the material in the book come to life in a fun and meaningful way.

Try these activities and have fun with math!

**Newspaper Hunt:** Numbers are all around us. With your child, scan a newspaper article to find large numbers. Highlight and discuss the numbers. Try comparing them, naming the values of different digits, switching around the order of the digits to make the largest and smallest possible numbers.

**Fact Review:** It is important that your child learn the multiplication facts. Have your child make and work with multiplication flash cards. Those facts that they have trouble remembering can be posted around the house in highly visited areas (the refrigerator door, the bathroom mirror, the TV remote). Once they achieve mastery, switch those cards for others which are causing difficulty.

The more fun you and your child have, the more likely he or she will be to develop a positive attitude towards mathematics. Good Luck and Have Fun!

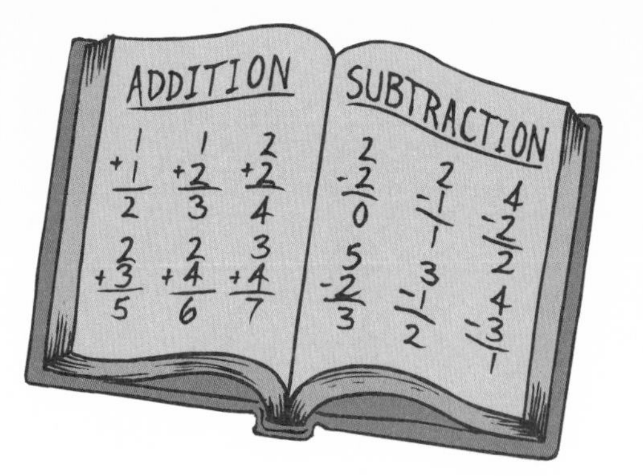

**This book is a companion book for the Smart Alec Series to Math Problem Solving book.**

# Table of Contents

# Place Value through the Millions

Did you know that lightning strikes about 259,200,000 times per month on our planet?

**word name:** two hundred fifty-nine million, two hundred thousand
**standard form:** 259,200,000
**expanded form:** 200,000,000 + 50,000,000 + 9,000,000 + 200,000

**Write each number in standard form and expanded form.**

1 seven million, two hundred four thousand, five hundred thirty-two

_______________________________________________

2 eighty-two million, one hundred seventeen thousand, eleven

_______________________________________________

**Place Value**

These are the place values for 643,927,860.

| one hundred million | ten million | million | one hundred thousand | ten thousand | one thousand | one hundred | ten | one |
|---|---|---|---|---|---|---|---|---|
| 6 | 4 | 3 | 9 | 2 | 7 | 8 | 6 | 0 |

**Write the name of the place value of the number in bold.**

**EXAMPLE** 7**4**6,208,015 ____ten million____

4 78, 3**4**2, 807 ______________________

5 **4**26, 786, 035 ______________________

6 623, **4**09, 672 ______________________

# Compare and Order Numbers

To compare numbers you start from the highest place value. Find the first place where the digits are different. Then compare those digits.

Compare 72,415 and 73,872

7**2**,415 7**3**,872

< means **less than**

> means **greater than**

= means **equals**

A crocodile facing left means greater than.

2 thousand 3 thousand so 72,415 73,872

**Compare** the numbers. Write <, >, or = in the circle.

1. 113,406 (>) 111,897
2. 472,654 ○ 475,862
3. fifteen thousand twenty ○ 15,020
4. 70,090 ○ seventy thousand ninety
5. 54 + 10 ○ 63 + 5
6. 116 + 4 ○ 124 − 4

**Order** the numbers from **least** to **greatest**.

7. 22,000 220,000 202,000 20,022

_______________________________________________

8. 17,707 717,077 77,117 71,770

_______________________________________________

**Write** the number.

9. Write the number that is two less than 6,789. ____________

10. Write the number that is ten more than 72,567. ____________

# Rounding Numbers

To round a number to the hundreds place first **underline** the hundreds place.

If the digit to the **right** of that number is **5 or higher**, increase the underlined digit by one and change the rest of the numbers on the right to zeros.

If the digit to the **right** of that number is **less than 5**, keep the underlined digit the same and change the rest of the numbers on the right to zeros.

Round **68,462** to the nearest hundred.

68,<u>4</u>**6**2 Underline the 4. Look at the 6. Since 6 is greater than 5, change the 4 to a 5 and change the rest of the numbers on the right to zeros.

68,462 rounded to the nearest hundred is 68,**500**

**Round** each number to the nearest **thousand**.

1. 52,614 — 53,000
2. 63,245 — ____________
3. 154,724 — ____________

**Round** each number to the place of the **underlined** digit.

4. 86,7<u>6</u>3 — ____________
5. 3<u>2</u>,784 — ____________
6. 18,<u>4</u>21 — ____________

7. **Round** 52,764 to the…

nearest **hundred**: ____________

nearest **thousand**: ____________

nearest **ten-thousand**: ____________

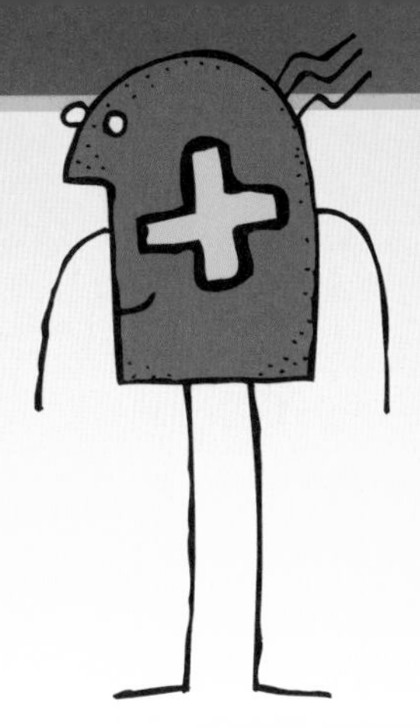

# Rounding and Estimation

Before adding, round each addend to its highest place value. Add those numbers to get an **estimate**. Check the actual **sum** against your **estimate** to see if it makes sense.

```
  1 1
  4,9 2 3 → rounds to  5,000
+   7 8 4 → rounds to  + 800
  5,7 0 7 → estimate:  5,800
```

actual sum: **5,707**

Since the actual sum is close to the estimate, the answer makes sense.

**Round each addend to the highest place value to come up with an estimate. Find the actual sum.**

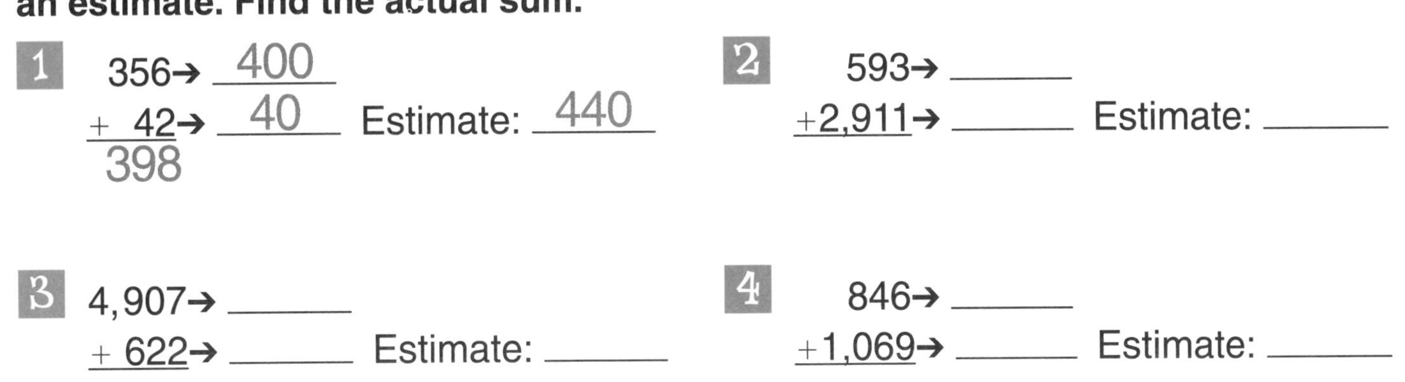

**1**
356→ 400
+ 42→ 40 Estimate: 440
398

**2**
593→ ______
+2,911→ ______ Estimate: ______

**3**
4,907→ ______
+ 622→ ______ Estimate: ______

**4**
846→ ______
+1,069→ ______ Estimate: ______

**Add. Regroup when necessary.**

**5** **Write and solve a number sentence for the problem.**

Pedro and Josette collect coins. If Pedro collected 2,567 coins and Josette collected 6,432 coins, how many coins did the children collect altogether? ____________________

# Animal Addition

If the **sum** is > 1,000, color the space dark brown.

If the **sum** is > 10,000, color the space light brown.

If the **sum** is < 1,000, choose your own color for the space.

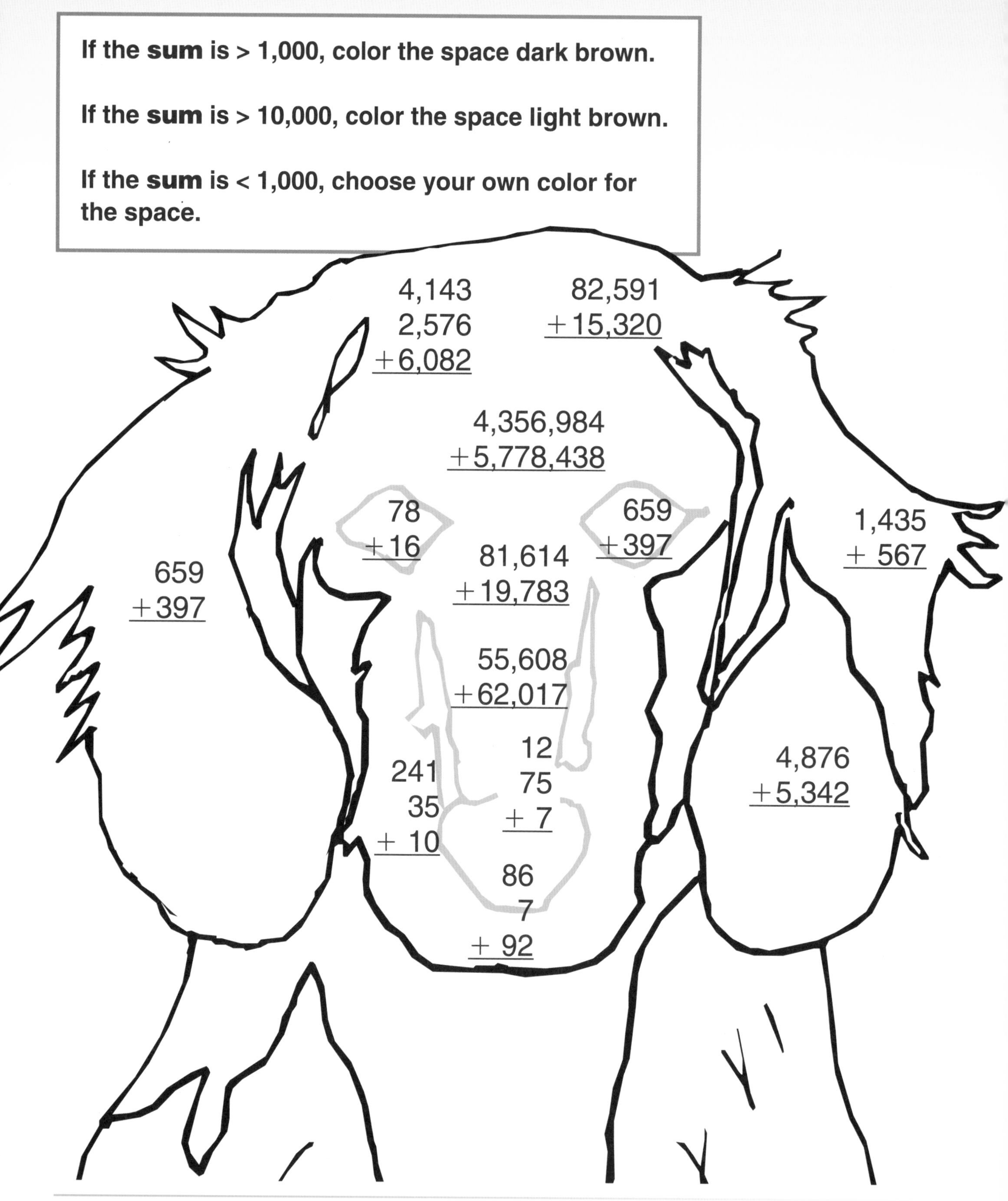

# Subtract with One Regrouping

Here's how to subtract with regrouping.

$$\begin{array}{r} \text{minuend} \\ -\ \text{subtrahend} \\ \hline \text{difference} \end{array}$$

Start by subtracting the ones. 5 − 3 = **2 ones**

$$\begin{array}{r} 465 \\ -\ 273 \\ \hline 2 \end{array}$$

Subtract the tens. Since you cannot subtract 7 from 6, **regroup** 4 hundreds and 6 tens into 3 hundreds and 16 tens. 16 − 7 = **9 tens**

$$\begin{array}{r} {}^{3}\not{4}{}^{1}65 \\ -\ 273 \\ \hline 92 \end{array}$$

Subtract the hundreds. 3 − 2 = **1 hundred**

$$\begin{array}{r} {}^{3}\not{4}{}^{1}65 \\ -\ 273 \\ \hline 192 \end{array}$$

The **difference** is 192.

To check your work, add the **difference** to the **subtrahend**, and see if you end up with the **minuend**.

$$\begin{array}{r} 192 \\ +\ 273 \\ \hline 465 \end{array}$$

**Subtract. Regroup** when necessary. **Check** your work.

**1** $\begin{array}{r} 82 \\ -\ 57 \\ \hline 25 \end{array}$ CHECK: $\begin{array}{r} 25 \\ +\ 57 \\ \hline 82 \end{array}$

**2** $\begin{array}{r} 45 \\ -\ 18 \\ \hline \end{array}$ CHECK: + ______

**3** $\begin{array}{r} 73 \\ -\ 44 \\ \hline \end{array}$ CHECK: + ______

**4** $\begin{array}{r} 285 \\ -\ 192 \\ \hline \end{array}$ CHECK: + ______

**5** $\begin{array}{r} 826 \\ -\ 575 \\ \hline \end{array}$ CHECK: + ______

**6** $\begin{array}{r} 734 \\ -\ 318 \\ \hline \end{array}$ CHECK: + ______

# Subtract and Regroup

Here's how to subtract with more than one regrouping.

Regroup 3 tens and 5 ones to 2 tens and 15 ones.
15 – 9 = **6 ones**

```
  2 1
 435
-279
   6
```

Regroup 4 hundreds and 2 tens to 3 hundreds and 12 tens.
12 – 7 = **5 tens**

```
3 12 1
 435
-279
  56
```

Subtract the hundreds. 3 – 2 = **1 hundred**

```
3 12 1
 435
-279
 156
```

## What did one math book say to the other?

**To find out, subtract and regroup when necessary.**
**Write the matching letter above each answer on the blank.**

```
  643          5,626          529
- 476        - 1,808        - 364
  167 = R             = L          = G

 4,357         9,325         1,439
 - 584       - 4,768         - 275
                      = A          = S

  432          6,317         2,548
 - 55        - 2,408       - 1,283
      = B             = T          = M

 8,356         4,672          482
- 5,679        - 853        - 304
      = E             = O          = P
```

M____n, h____ve I ____ ____ ____ ____ ____ ____ ____ ____ ____ ____ ____!

(4,557) (4,557) — 165 3,819 3,909 178 167 3,819 377 3,818 2,677 1,265 1,164

# Subtract with Zeros

Here's how to subtract with zeros.

| | |
|---|---|
| $\begin{array}{r} {}^{6\,10} \\ \not{7}00 \\ -\ 574 \\ \hline \end{array}$ | Start by subtracting the ones. Since you cannot subtract 4 from 0, try regrouping the tens. There are no tens. Regroup 7 hundreds to 6 hundreds and 10 tens. |
| $\begin{array}{r} {}^{6\ 9\,10} \\ \not{7}\not{0}\not{0} \\ -\ 574 \\ \hline \end{array}$ | Now that you have tens, regroup 10 tens to 9 tens and 10 ones. |
| $\begin{array}{r} {}^{6\ 9\,10} \\ \not{7}\not{0}\not{0} \\ -\ 574 \\ \hline \end{array}$ | Now, you can subtract starting from the ones.<br>$10 - 4 = 6$<br>$9 - 7 = 2$<br>$6 - 5 = 1$ The **difference** is **126**. |

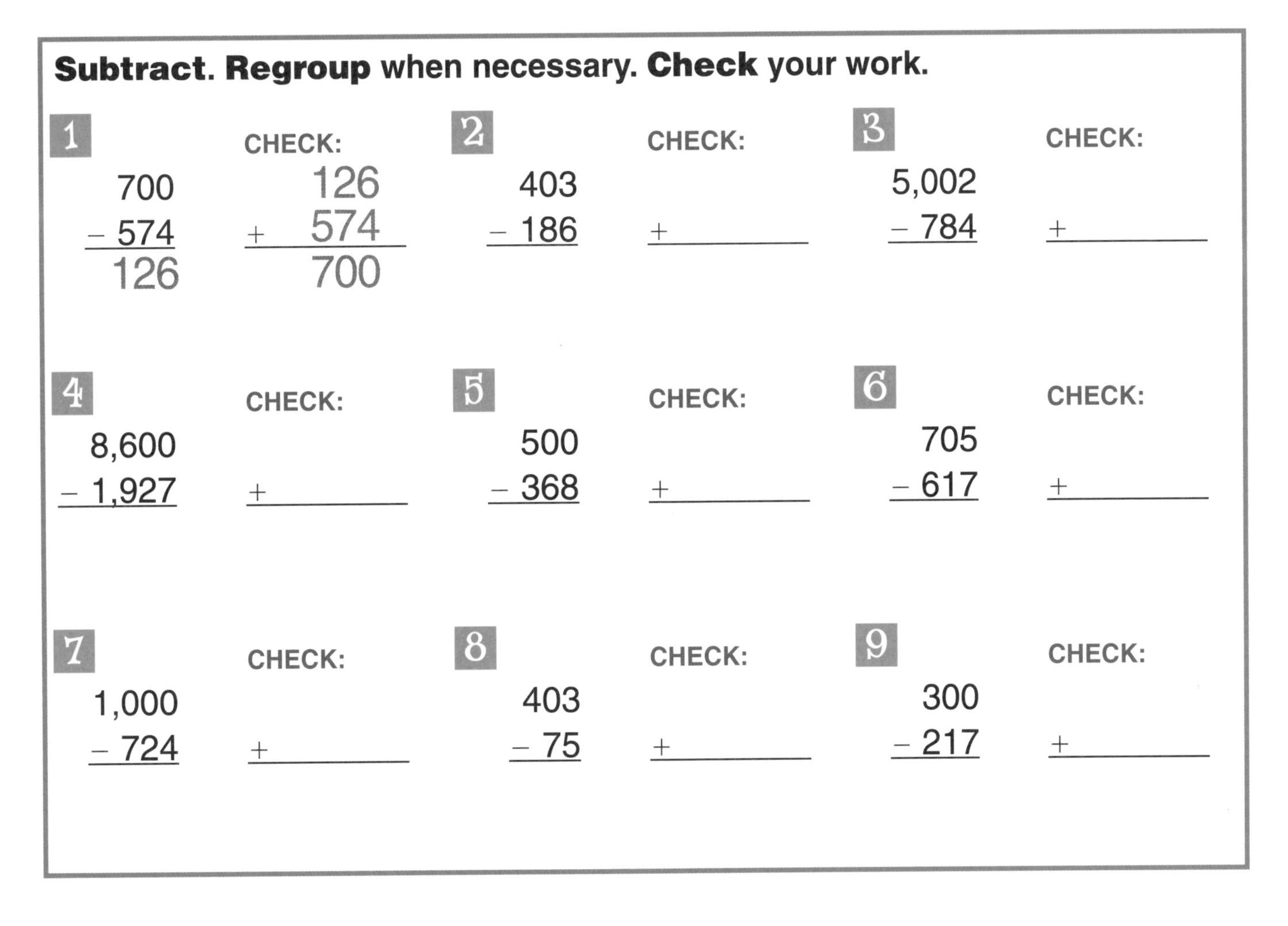

**Subtract. Regroup** when necessary. **Check** your work.

**1**
$\begin{array}{r} 700 \\ -\ 574 \\ \hline 126 \end{array}$ CHECK: $\begin{array}{r} 126 \\ +\ 574 \\ \hline 700 \end{array}$

**2**
$\begin{array}{r} 403 \\ -\ 186 \\ \hline \end{array}$ CHECK: $+$ ______

**3**
$\begin{array}{r} 5{,}002 \\ -\ 784 \\ \hline \end{array}$ CHECK: $+$ ______

**4**
$\begin{array}{r} 8{,}600 \\ -\ 1{,}927 \\ \hline \end{array}$ CHECK: $+$ ______

**5**
$\begin{array}{r} 500 \\ -\ 368 \\ \hline \end{array}$ CHECK: $+$ ______

**6**
$\begin{array}{r} 705 \\ -\ 617 \\ \hline \end{array}$ CHECK: $+$ ______

**7**
$\begin{array}{r} 1{,}000 \\ -\ 724 \\ \hline \end{array}$ CHECK: $+$ ______

**8**
$\begin{array}{r} 403 \\ -\ 75 \\ \hline \end{array}$ CHECK: $+$ ______

**9**
$\begin{array}{r} 300 \\ -\ 217 \\ \hline \end{array}$ CHECK: $+$ ______

# Numbers, Adding, and Subtracting

**Use the clues to complete the crossword puzzle below.**

## ACROSS

**4.** 700 + 482

**7.** 78,604 to the nearest hundred

**8.** 974 + 798

**10.** eight million eight hundred forty seven thousand three hundred ten

**11.** four thousand seven hundred fifteen

**13.** 50,000 + 7,000 + 17

**14.** 1000 - 692

## DOWN

**1.** 700 + 50 + 8

**2.** 412,345 to the nearest ten thousand

**3.** 1,200,000 – 39,693

**5.** 985 – 698

**6.** the difference between 201 and 99

**8.** the sum of 675 and 482

**9.** 65,872 + 12,304

**12.** 4,672 to the nearest thousand

# Multiplication Facts

factor
× factor
product

Find as many multiplication facts as you can. You may look across, down, forward, backward, and diagonally.

Write the facts that you find on the lines below in number sentence form. The first one is done for you.

| | | | | | | | | | |
|---|---|---|---|---|---|---|---|---|---|
| 7 | 9 | 63 | 5 | 1 | 18 | 3 | 6 | 7 | 42 |
| 2 | 3 | 6 | 4 | 4 | 6 | 24 | 3 | 9 | 5 |
| 14 | 27 | 9 | 4 | 3 | 20 | 9 | 18 | 63 | 8 |
| 48 | 8 | 54 | 16 | 12 | 4 | 5 | 9 | 4 | 40 |
| 8 | 7 | 56 | 5 | 2 | 9 | 45 | 3 | 81 | 10 |
| 6 | 5 | 2 | 10 | 24 | 36 | 6 | 6 | 12 | 4 |
| 82 | 35 | 40 | 4 | 8 | 8 | 7 | 5 | 35 | 2 |

$7 \times 9 = 63$

# Estimate and Multiply

## Multiplying by 10

**When you multiply by 10, multiply the numbers first and then attach the total number of zeros in the factors.**

| $20 \times 7 = 140$ | $30 \times 60 = 1,800$ | $400 \times 50 = 20,000$ |
|---|---|---|
| ↓ | ↓ | ↓ |
| $2 \times 7 = 14$ | $3 \times 6 = 18$ | $4 \times 5 = 20$ |
| and attach one zero | and attach two zeros | and attach three zeros |
| 140 | 1,800 | 20,000 |

## Rounding Factors to Estimate Products

**Before multiplying, round each factor to its highest place value. Multiply to get an estimate.**

4,786 → rounds to 5,000
× 42 → rounds to 40

→ estimate:
$5 \times 4 = 20$
and attach four zeros
200,000

**Round each factor to the highest place value. Estimate a product. Find the actual product.**

1. 936 → 1000
   × 42 → 40 estimate: 40,000
   39,312

2. 693 → ______
   × 71 → ______ estimate: ______

3. 5,907 → ______
   × 822 → ______ estimate: ______

4. 846 → ______
   × 19 → ______ estimate: ______

5. 5,507 → ______
   × 462 → ______ estimate: ______

6. 446 → ______
   × 47 → ______ estimate: ______

# Multiply with Regrouping

Here's how to multiply with regrouping.

Start by multiplying the ones.
6 × 3 = **18 ones**

$$\begin{array}{r} \overset{1}{7}26 \\ \underline{\times \quad 3} \\ 8 \end{array}$$

Multiply the **tens**.
2 × 3 = **6 tens**
Regroup as needed.
6 tens + 1 ten = 7 tens.

$$\begin{array}{r} \overset{1}{7}26 \\ \underline{\times \quad 3} \\ 78 \end{array}$$

Multiply the **hundreds**.
7 × 3 = **21 hundreds**.

$$\begin{array}{r} \overset{1}{7}26 \\ \underline{\times \quad 3} \\ 2{,}178 \end{array}$$

The **product** is 2,178.

To check your work, round each factor to get an estimate.
Your actual answer should be close to your estimate.

$$\begin{array}{rcr} 726 & \rightarrow & 700 \\ \underline{\times \quad 3} & \rightarrow & \underline{\times \quad 3} \\ 2{,}178 & \rightarrow & 2{,}100 \end{array}$$

2,100 is close to the actual product of 2,178.

**Multiply, regroup** when necessary. **Check** your work using estimation.

**1**
$$\begin{array}{r} 62 \\ \underline{\times 8} \\ 496 \end{array}$$
CHECK:
$$\begin{array}{r} 60 \\ \underline{\times \quad 8} \\ 480 \end{array}$$

**2**
$$\begin{array}{r} 49 \\ \underline{\times 7} \end{array}$$
CHECK: × _____

**3**
$$\begin{array}{r} 27 \\ \underline{\times 4} \end{array}$$
CHECK: × _____

**4**
$$\begin{array}{r} 67 \\ \underline{\times 8} \end{array}$$
CHECK: × _____

**5**
$$\begin{array}{r} 284 \\ \underline{\times \quad 2} \end{array}$$
CHECK: × _____

**6**
$$\begin{array}{r} 118 \\ \underline{\times \quad 5} \end{array}$$
CHECK: × _____

**7**
$$\begin{array}{r} 712 \\ \underline{\times \quad 8} \end{array}$$
CHECK: × _____

**8**
$$\begin{array}{r} 504 \\ \underline{\times \quad 3} \end{array}$$
CHECK: × _____

# Multiplying Two Digit Numbers

Multiply each digit in the top factor by the ones of the **bottom factor**.
87 × 3 = **261** by the ones of the bottom factor.

$$\begin{array}{r} {}^{2}87 \\ \underline{\times\ 43} \\ 261 \end{array}$$

Place a zero in the ones column as a place holder.

$$\begin{array}{r} 87 \\ \underline{\times\ 43} \\ 261 \\ \underline{0} \end{array}$$

Multiply each digit in the top factor by the tens of the **bottom factor**.
87 × 4 = **348**

Add the numbers.
261 + 3,480 = **3,741**

$$\begin{array}{r} 87 \\ \underline{\times\ 43} \\ 261 \\ \underline{+3{,}480} \\ 3{,}741 \end{array}$$

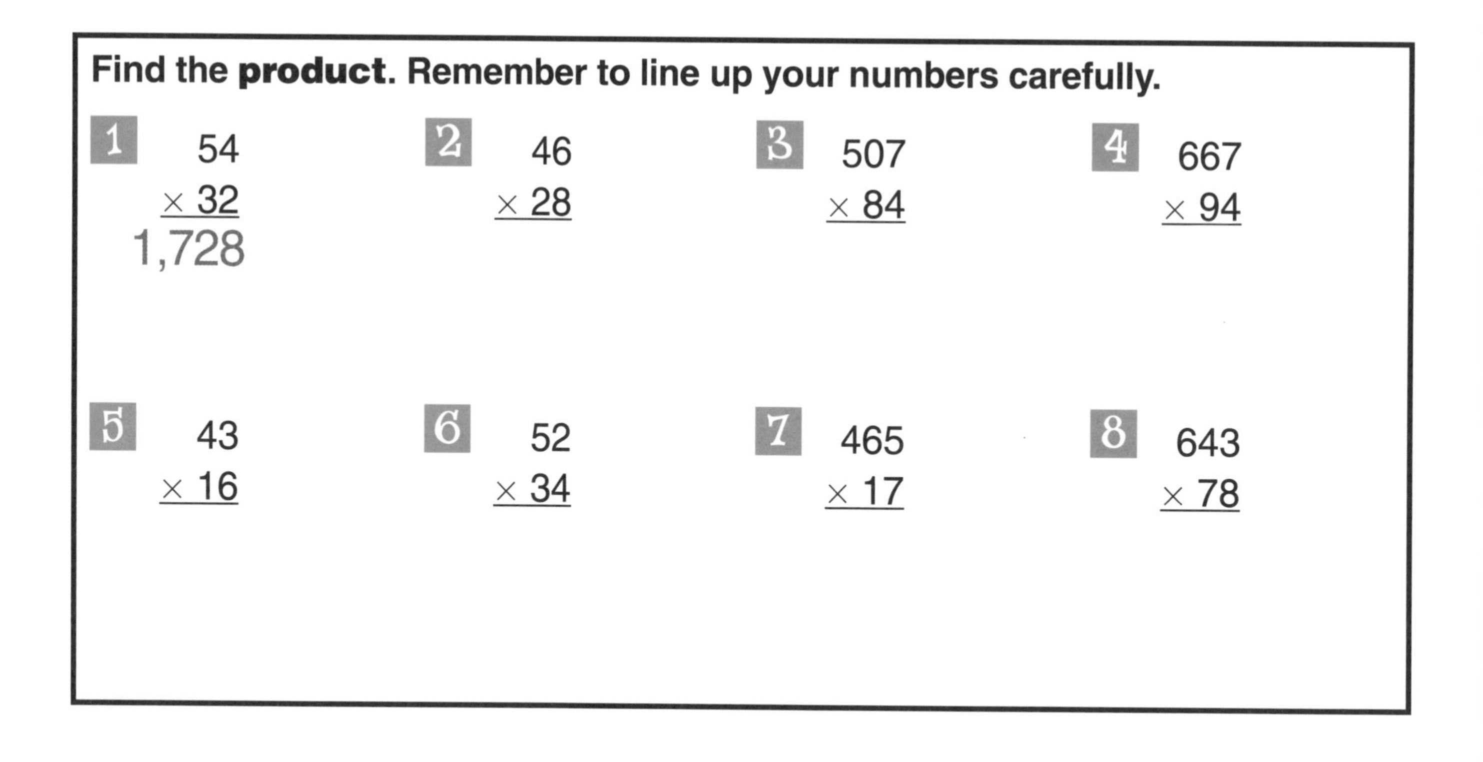

**Find the product.** Remember to line up your numbers carefully.

1. $\begin{array}{r} 54 \\ \underline{\times\ 32} \end{array}$ 1,728

2. $\begin{array}{r} 46 \\ \underline{\times\ 28} \end{array}$

3. $\begin{array}{r} 507 \\ \underline{\times\ 84} \end{array}$

4. $\begin{array}{r} 667 \\ \underline{\times\ 94} \end{array}$

5. $\begin{array}{r} 43 \\ \underline{\times\ 16} \end{array}$

6. $\begin{array}{r} 52 \\ \underline{\times\ 34} \end{array}$

7. $\begin{array}{r} 465 \\ \underline{\times\ 17} \end{array}$

8. $\begin{array}{r} 643 \\ \underline{\times\ 78} \end{array}$

# Multiply Two Digit Numbers

## What is it?

It appears once in a minute, twice in a week, and once in a year.

**To find out, multiply. Write the matching letter on the blank space above the answers at the bottom of the page.**

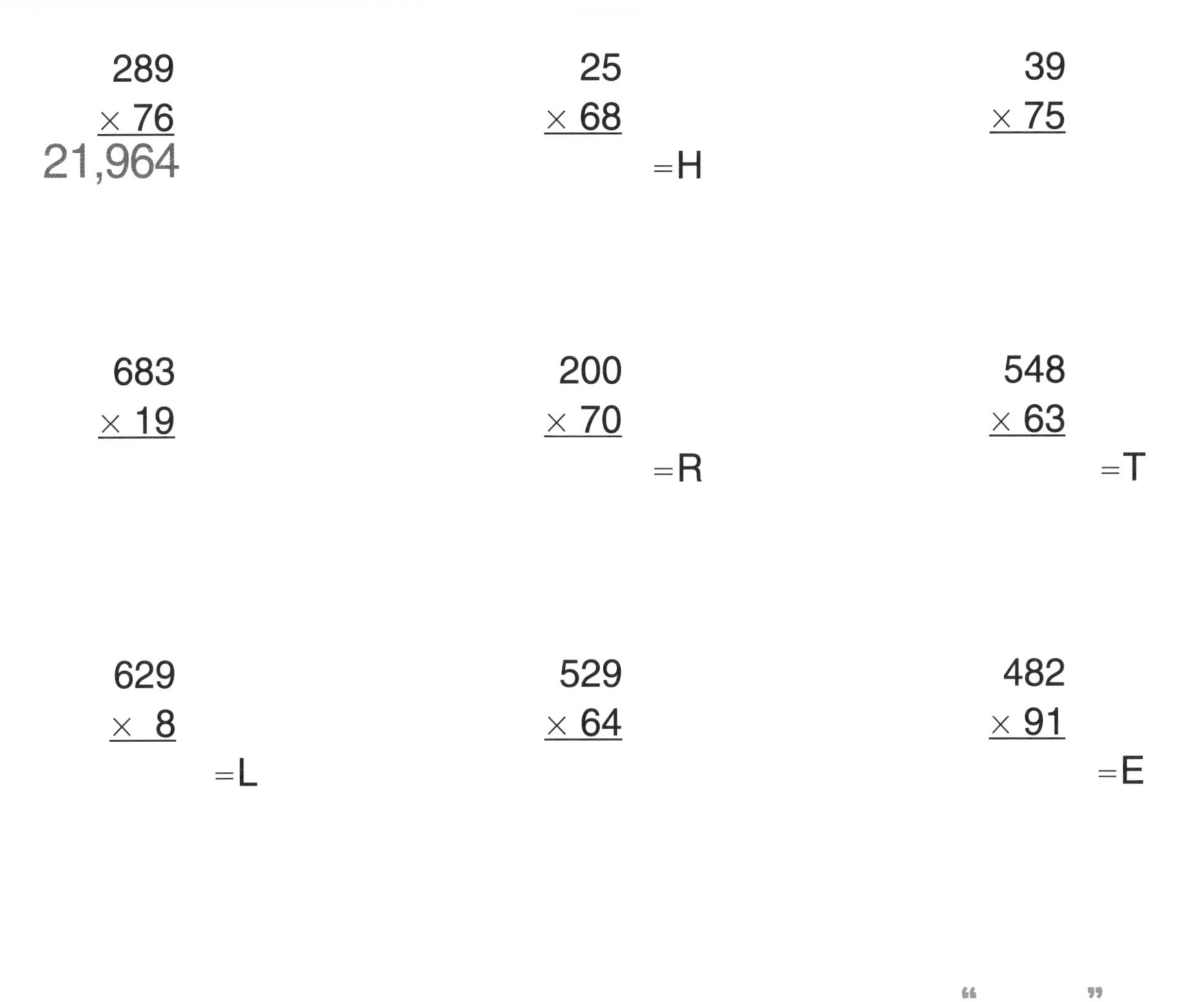

289
× 76
21,964
25
× 68
=H
39
× 75
683
× 19
200
× 70
=R
548
× 63
=T
629
× 8
=L
529
× 64
482
× 91
=E

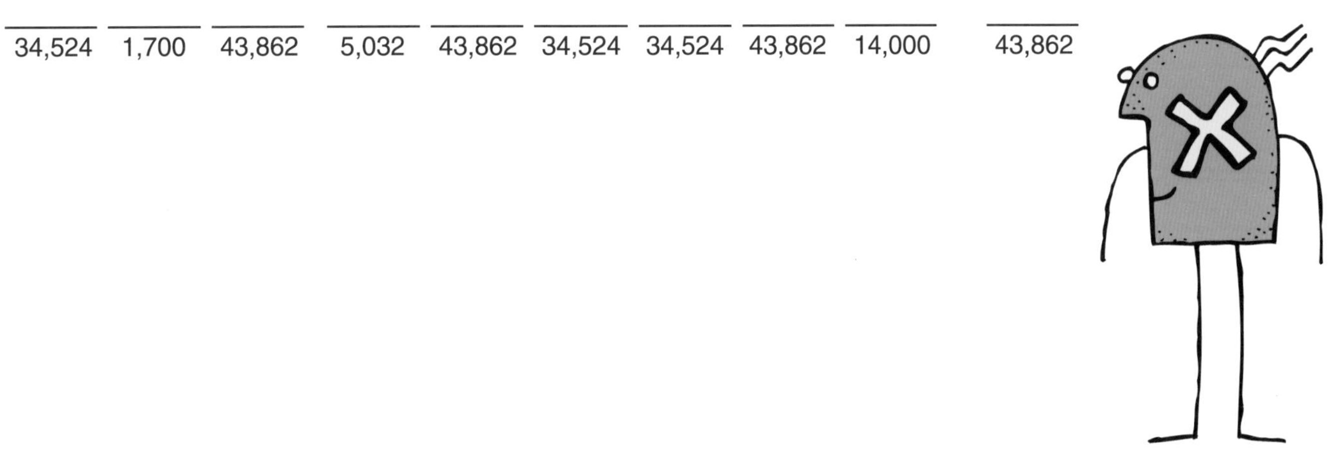

34,524
1,700
43,862
5,032
43,862
34,524
34,524
43,862
14,000
“ 43,862 ”

# Estimate and Divide

Here's how to use division facts you know to estimate a quotient.

To estimate a quotient, think of a division fact you know. **34 ÷ 8**

QUOTIENT
DIVISOR )DIVIDEND

OR

32 ÷ 8 = 4. The fact is close, but not too large. **34 ÷ 8 is about 4.**

DIVIDEND ÷ DIVISOR = QUOTIENT

**Estimate** the quotient. **Write** the division fact you know under each problem.

1 65 ÷ 8 is about 8.

64 ÷ 8 = 8

2 75 ÷ 8 is about _____.

________________

3 36 ÷ 5 is about _____.

________________

4 49 ÷ 6 is about _____.

________________

5 65 ÷ 9 is about _____.

________________

6 19 ÷ 3 is about _____.

________________

7 33 ÷ 8 is about _____.

________________

8 37 ÷ 6 is about _____.

________________

# Division with Remainders

**Often, one number can not be evenly divided by another number. In this case, there are leftovers. In math, we call the leftovers a remainder.**

**EXAMPLE** The clown divides **25** balloons among **4** children. Each child gets **6** balloons. There is **1** balloon leftover.

**Divide**

$$\begin{array}{r} 4 \\ 6\overline{)25} \end{array}$$

**Multiply**

$$\begin{array}{r} 4 \\ 6\overline{)25} \\ \underline{24} \end{array}$$

**Subtract**

$$\begin{array}{r} 4 \\ 6\overline{)25} \\ -\underline{24} \\ 1 \end{array}$$

**Remainder**

The number 1 can not be divided by 6. The 1 is left over and becomes a remainder.

The quotient is 4 R1.

To check, multiply the quotient by the divisor. Then, add the remainder. Your answer should be the dividend.

$$\begin{array}{rl} 4 & \text{quotient} \\ \underline{\times 6} & \underline{\text{divisor}} \\ 24 & \\ \underline{+ 1} & \underline{\text{remainder}} \\ 25 & \text{dividend} \end{array}$$

**Divide. Check your answer.**

**1**

$$\begin{array}{r} 6\text{ R2} \\ 3\overline{)20} \end{array}$$

CHECK

$$\begin{array}{r} 6 \\ \underline{\times 3} \\ 18 \\ \underline{+2} \\ 20 \end{array}$$

**2** $7\overline{)52}$ CHECK

**3** $5\overline{)42}$ CHECK

**4** $6\overline{)39}$ CHECK

**5** $4\overline{)38}$ CHECK

**6** $8\overline{)75}$ CHECK

# More Division

Here's how to divide with a two-digit quotient. For example, consider $3\overline{)74}$.

Divide the tens. $\begin{array}{r} 2 \\ 3\overline{)74} \\ -6\phantom{4} \\ \hline 1\phantom{4} \end{array}$

Bring down the ones. Divide the divisor by what is left, and repeat the steps until there are no more digits to bring down.

Problem: $\begin{array}{r} 24 \text{ R2} \\ 3\overline{)74}\phantom{\text{ R2}} \\ -6\phantom{4}\phantom{\text{ R2}} \\ \hline 14\phantom{\text{ R2}} \\ -12\phantom{\text{ R2}} \\ \hline 2\phantom{\text{ R2}} \end{array}$

Check: $\begin{array}{r} 24 \\ \times\ 3 \\ \hline 72 \\ +2 \\ \hline 74 \end{array}$

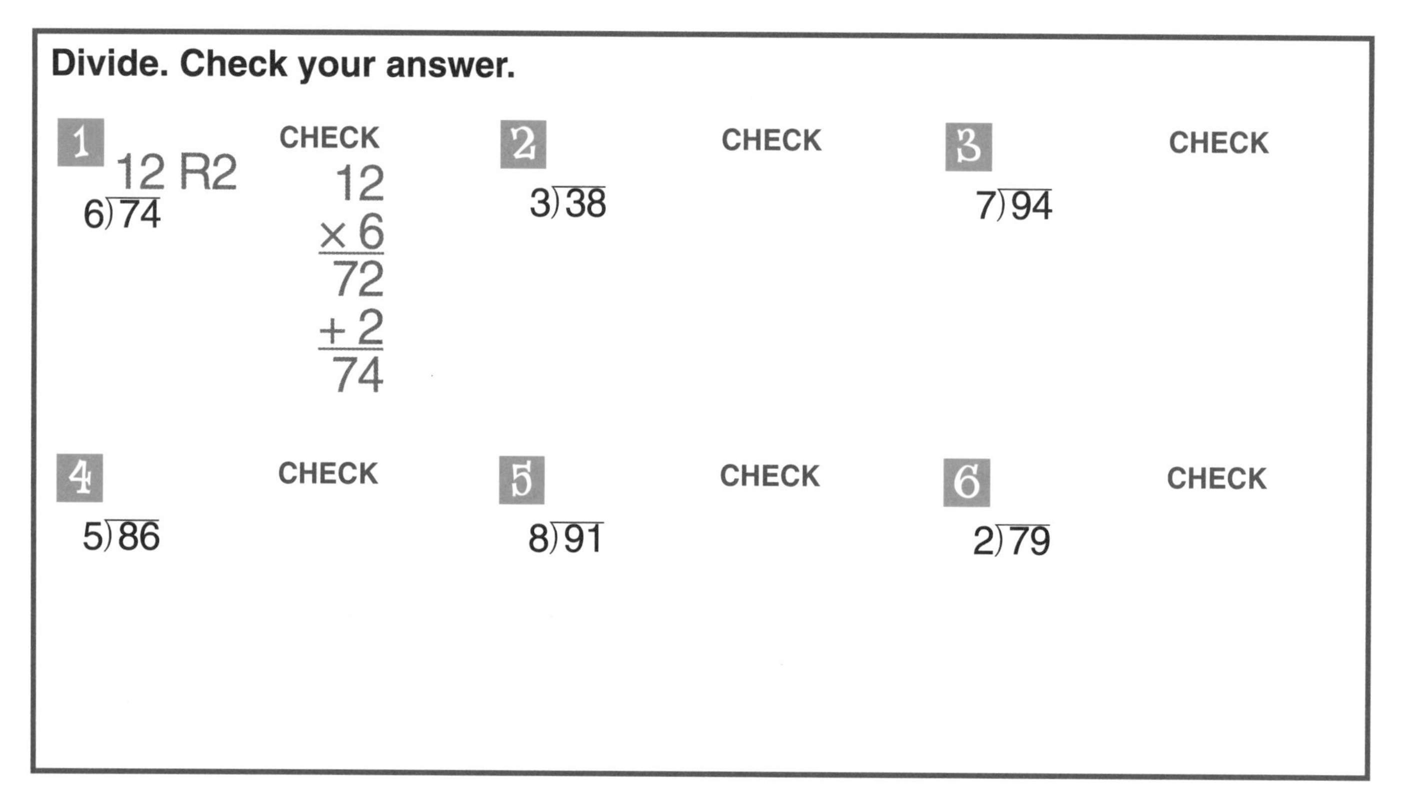

**Divide. Check your answer.**

**1** $\begin{array}{r} 12 \text{ R2} \\ 6\overline{)74}\phantom{\text{ R2}} \end{array}$ CHECK $\begin{array}{r} 12 \\ \times\ 6 \\ \hline 72 \\ +\ 2 \\ \hline 74 \end{array}$

**2** $3\overline{)38}$ CHECK

**3** $7\overline{)94}$ CHECK

**4** $5\overline{)86}$ CHECK

**5** $8\overline{)91}$ CHECK

**6** $2\overline{)79}$ CHECK

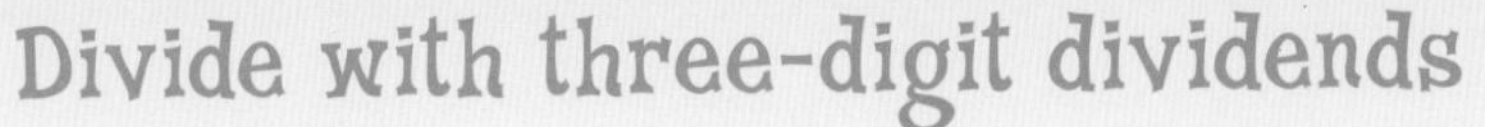

# Divide with three-digit dividends

The first digit of the quotient does not always go directly above the first digit of the dividend. You need to decide where to place it. Find the first place where the divisor can be divided into the dividend. Then place the first digit of the quotient above that number.

```
    84 R3
 4)339
  -32
    19
   -16
     3
```

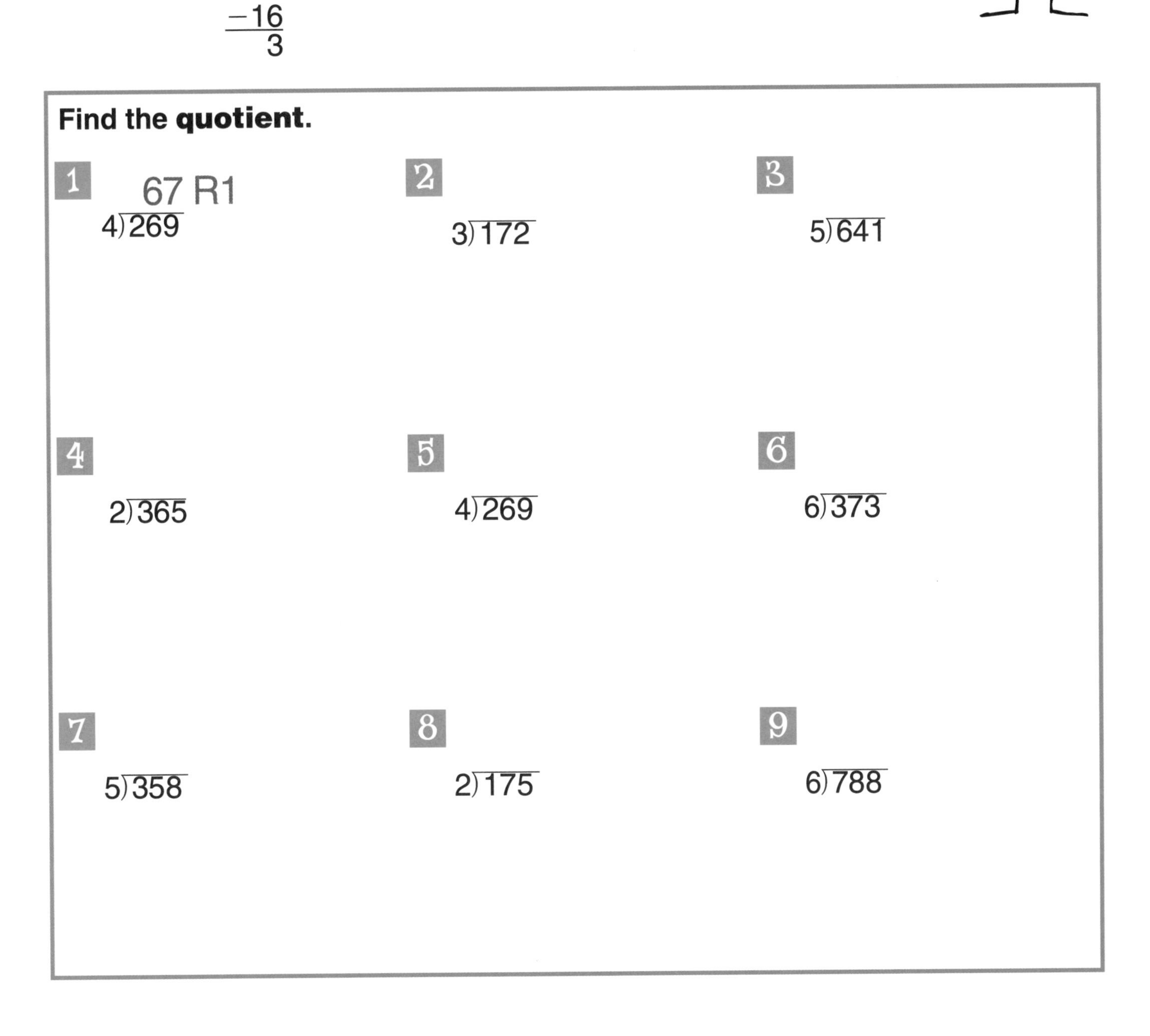

**Find the quotient.**

1. $4\overline{)269}$ = 67 R1

2. $3\overline{)172}$

3. $5\overline{)641}$

4. $2\overline{)365}$

5. $4\overline{)269}$

6. $6\overline{)373}$

7. $5\overline{)358}$

8. $2\overline{)175}$

9. $6\overline{)788}$

# Zeros in the Quotient

**Watch out for zeros in the quotient!**

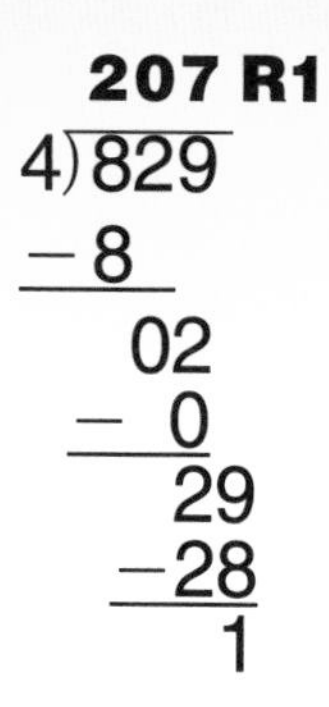


Since 2 cannot be divided by 4, place a zero in the quotient and keep working.

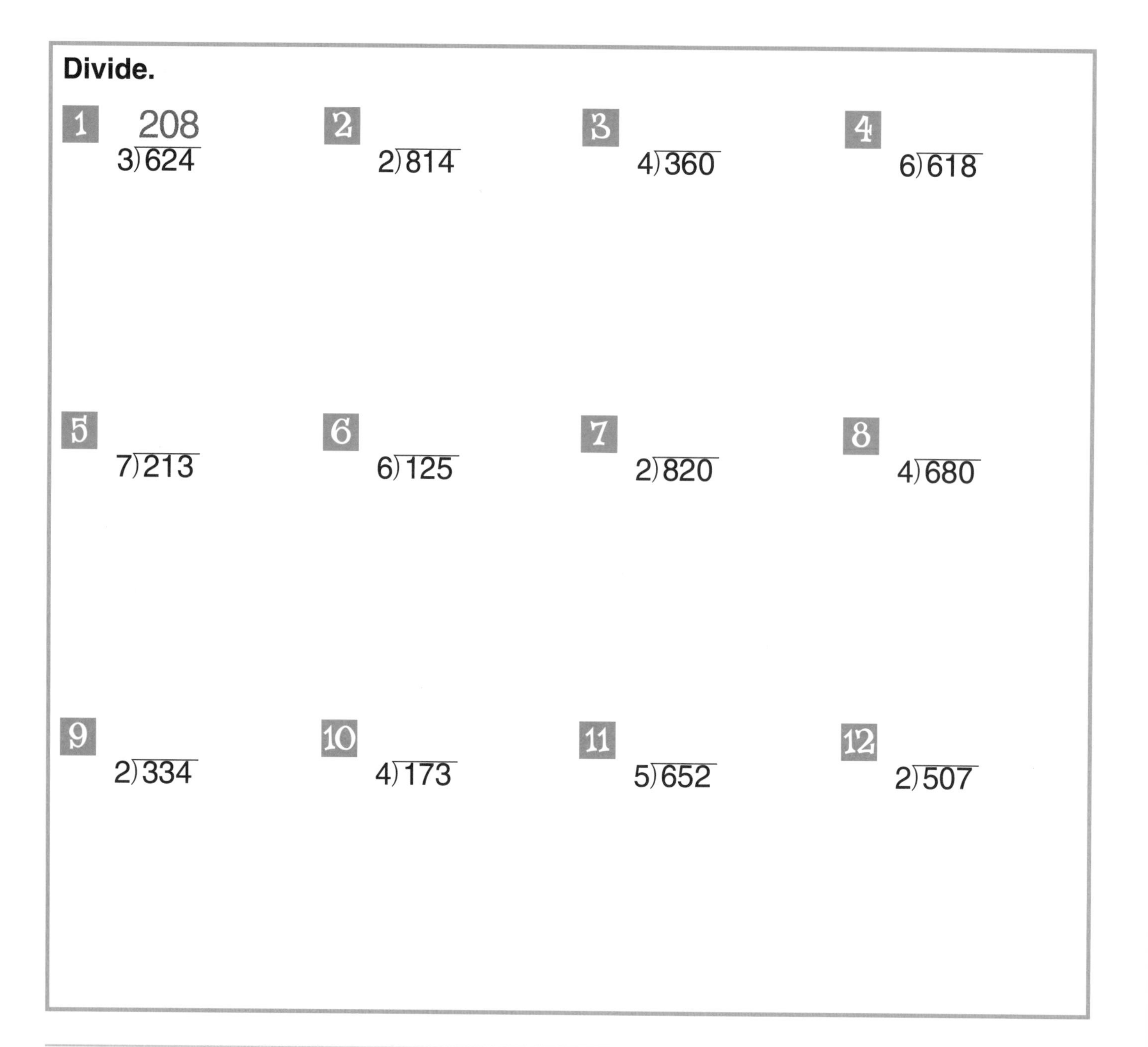

**Divide.**

1. $3\overline{)624}$ 208
2. $2\overline{)814}$
3. $4\overline{)360}$
4. $6\overline{)618}$
5. $7\overline{)213}$
6. $6\overline{)125}$
7. $2\overline{)820}$
8. $4\overline{)680}$
9. $2\overline{)334}$
10. $4\overline{)173}$
11. $5\overline{)652}$
12. $2\overline{)507}$

# Divide with Two-Digit Divisors

You divide with a two-digit divisor the same way you would with a one-digit divisor.

1. Look at the dividend. Find the first place that the divisor can divide. In this case, it will be the tens place.

   $65\overline{)739}$

2. Estimate a product that is close to 700.
   $65 \times 10 = 650$
   Then, subtract.

   $$\begin{array}{r} 1\phantom{9} \\ 65\overline{)739} \\ -\underline{65}\phantom{9} \\ 89 \end{array}$$

3. Continue dividing by estimating a product and then subtracting.

   $$\begin{array}{r} 11 \text{ R24} \\ 65\overline{)739} \\ -\underline{65}\phantom{9} \\ 89 \\ -\underline{65} \\ 24 \end{array}$$

**Divide.**

1. $65\overline{)739}$   11 R24
2. $36\overline{)975}$
3. $41\overline{)885}$
4. $92\overline{)4,422}$
5. $38\overline{)765}$
6. $27\overline{)1,231}$

# Understand Fractions

Fractions can show part of a set or part of a whole.

$\frac{3}{8}$ → numerator, denominator

**Part of a set**

$3$ → number of shaded objects
$8$ → total number of objects

**Part of a whole**

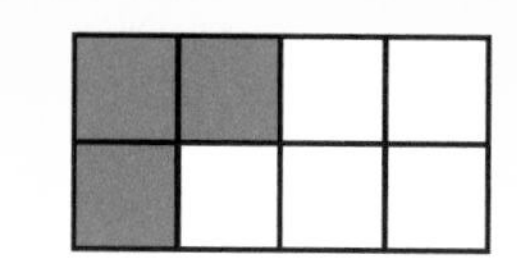

$3$ → number of shaded parts
$8$ → total number of parts

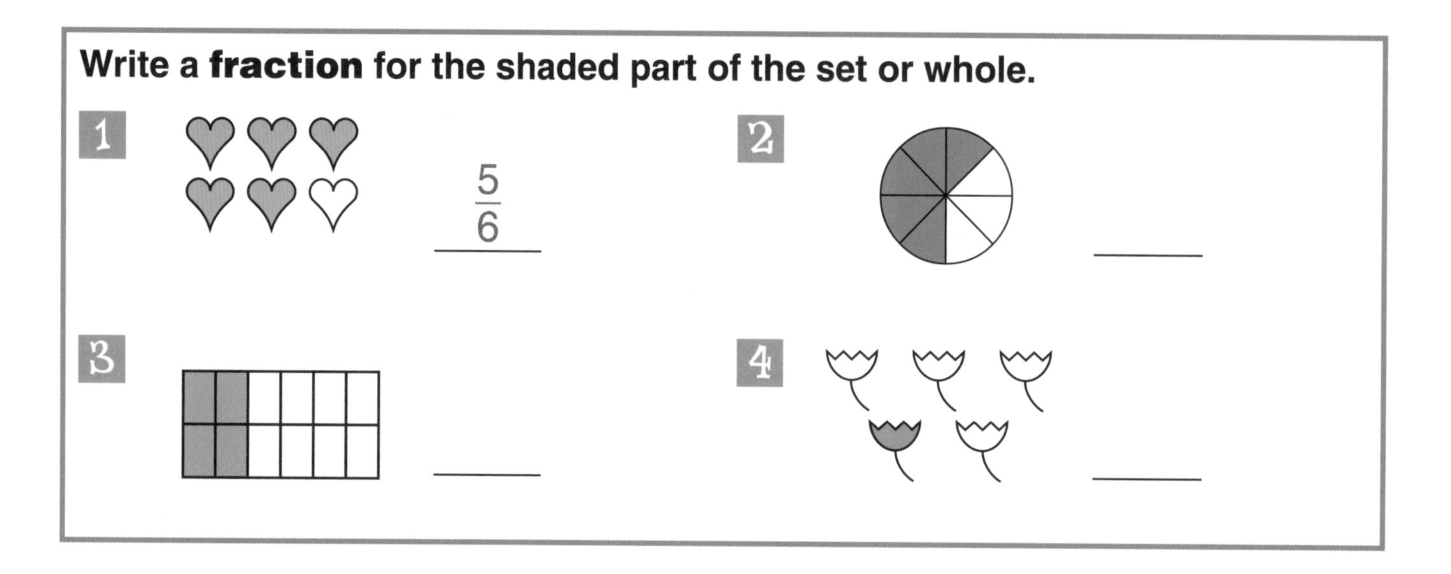

Write a **fraction** for the shaded part of the set or whole.
1
5
6
2
3
4


**Use the fraction to help you shade part of the set or whole.**

5 $\frac{2}{3}$

6 $\frac{3}{5}$

7 $\frac{3}{4}$

# Find Equivalent Fractions

Equivalent fractions are fractions that name the same amount in a different way.

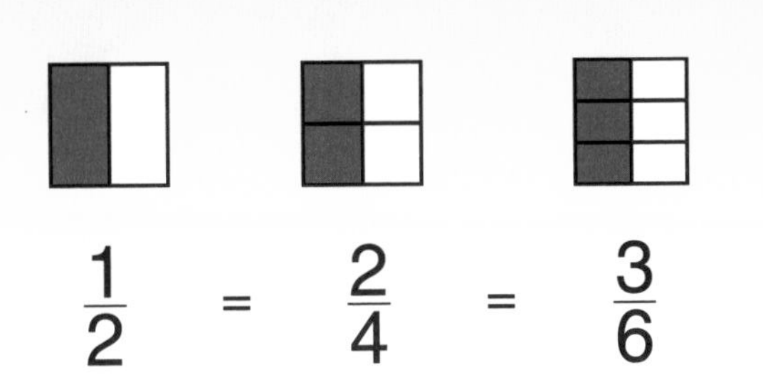

$\frac{1}{2} = \frac{2}{4} = \frac{3}{6}$

To find equivalent fractions, you can multiply or divide both the numerator and the denominator by the same number.

$$\frac{1 \times 2}{2 \times 2} = \frac{2}{4} \text{ or } \frac{3 \div 3}{6 \div 3} = \frac{1}{2}$$

**Write the missing numerator. The first one is done for you.**

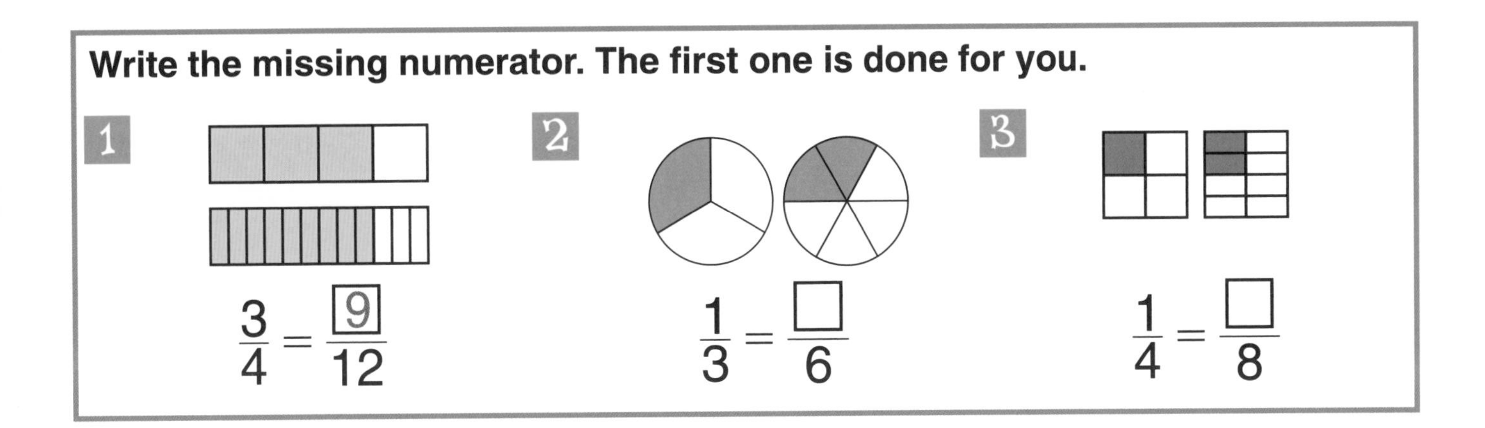

1. $\frac{3}{4} = \frac{9}{12}$

2. $\frac{1}{3} = \frac{\square}{6}$

3. $\frac{1}{4} = \frac{\square}{8}$

**Multiply** or **Divide** to find the equivalent fraction.

4. $\frac{4 \div 4}{8 \div 4} = \frac{1}{2}$

5. $\frac{1}{3} = \frac{\phantom{0}}{9}$

6. $\frac{16}{20} = \frac{\phantom{0}}{5}$

7. $\frac{3}{21} = \frac{\phantom{0}}{7}$

8. $\frac{2}{7} = \frac{\phantom{0}}{14}$

9. $\frac{4}{9} = \frac{\phantom{0}}{27}$

10. $\frac{2}{10} = \frac{\phantom{0}}{20}$

11. $\frac{3}{5} = \frac{\phantom{0}}{15}$

12. $\frac{7}{21} = \frac{\phantom{0}}{3}$

# Compare Fractions

**When comparing fractions with like denominators, simply compare numerators.**

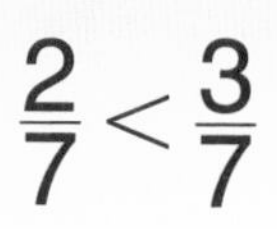

$\frac{2}{7} < \frac{3}{7}$ 2 is less than 3, so $\frac{2}{7}$ is less than $\frac{3}{7}$.

**When comparing fractions with unlike denominators, find an equivalent fraction with the same denominator. Then, compare.**

$\frac{1}{3} \bigcirc \frac{5}{6}$ Convert $\frac{1}{3}$ to sixths by multiplying both the numerator and the denominator by 2.

$$\frac{1 \times 2}{3 \times 2} = \frac{2}{6}$$

**Now that both fractions have a common denominator, you can compare them by looking at the numerators.**

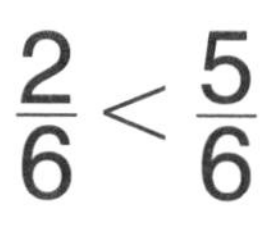

$\frac{2}{6} < \frac{5}{6}$

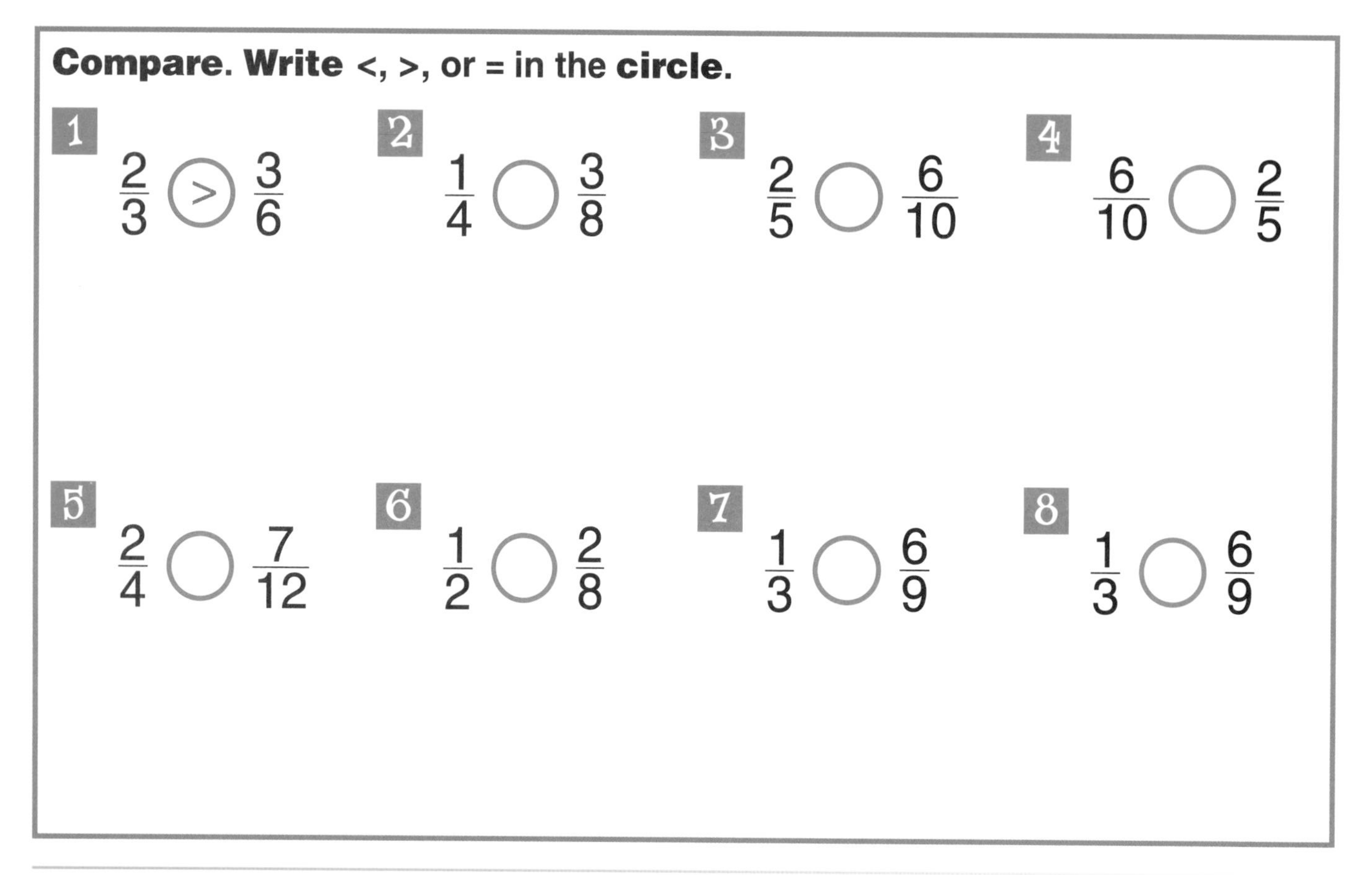

**Compare. Write <, >, or = in the circle.**

1. $\frac{2}{3}$ (>) $\frac{3}{6}$
2. $\frac{1}{4} \bigcirc \frac{3}{8}$
3. $\frac{2}{5} \bigcirc \frac{6}{10}$
4. $\frac{6}{10} \bigcirc \frac{2}{5}$
5. $\frac{2}{4} \bigcirc \frac{7}{12}$
6. $\frac{1}{2} \bigcirc \frac{2}{8}$
7. $\frac{1}{3} \bigcirc \frac{6}{9}$
8. $\frac{1}{3} \bigcirc \frac{6}{9}$

# Fractions in Simplest Form

**A fraction is in simplest form when both the numerator and denominator cannot be divided by any number other than 1.**

$\frac{5}{6}$ is in simplest form. Both 5 and 6 cannot be divided by any number other than 1.

$\frac{16}{20}$ is NOT in simplest form. Both the numerator and denominator can be divided by 4 or by 2.

To simplify the fraction, divide both the numerator and denominator by the same number.

$$\frac{16 \div 4}{20 \div 4} = \frac{4}{5} \quad \text{or} \quad \frac{16 \div 2}{20 \div 2} = \frac{8 \div 2}{10 \div 2} = \frac{4}{5}$$

Can you find another number that can be divided into both 4 and 5?
No. Then it is in the simplest form.

**Is each fraction in simplest form? Circle yes or no.**
**If a fraction is not in its simplest form, simplify it.**

1. $\frac{5}{6}$ (yes) no ____
2. $\frac{3}{7}$ yes no ____
3. $\frac{2}{6}$ yes no ____
4. $\frac{5}{9}$ yes no ____
5. $\frac{6}{24}$ yes no ____
6. $\frac{3}{15}$ yes no ____

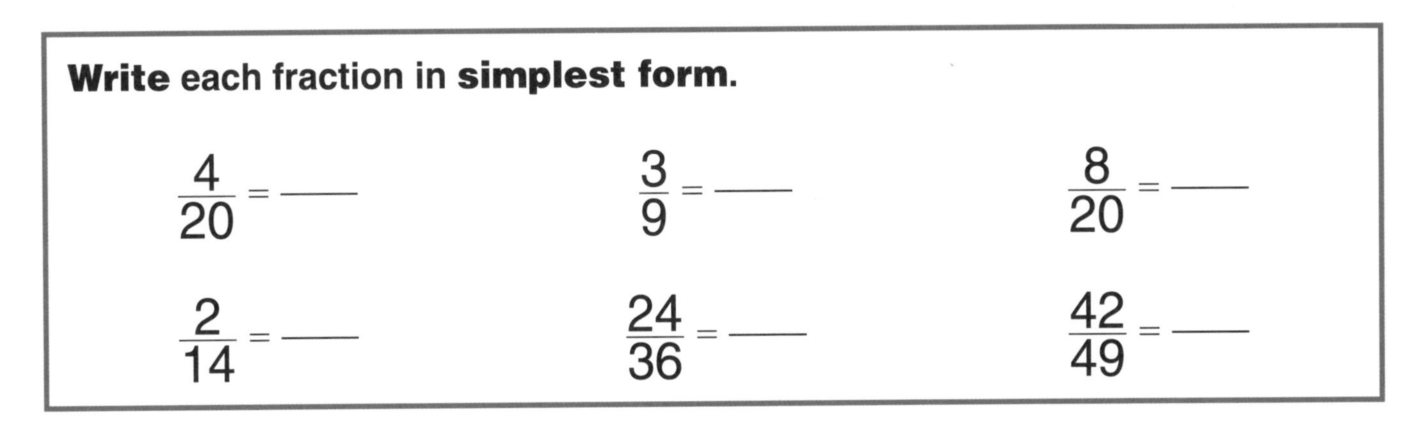

**Write each fraction in simplest form.**

$\frac{4}{20}$ = ____ $\frac{3}{9}$ = ____ $\frac{8}{20}$ = ____

$\frac{2}{14}$ = ____ $\frac{24}{36}$ = ____ $\frac{42}{49}$ = ____

# Mixed Numbers

A mixed number is a whole number with a fraction.

$$2\frac{1}{2}, 1\frac{3}{4}, 5\frac{4}{7}$$

An improper fraction is a fraction whose numerator is larger than its denominator.

$$\frac{8}{7}, \frac{20}{9}, \frac{11}{2}$$

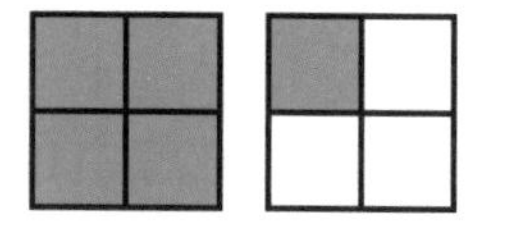

Notice how this picture can be seen as $\frac{5}{4}$ (improper) or $1\frac{1}{4}$ (a mixed number).

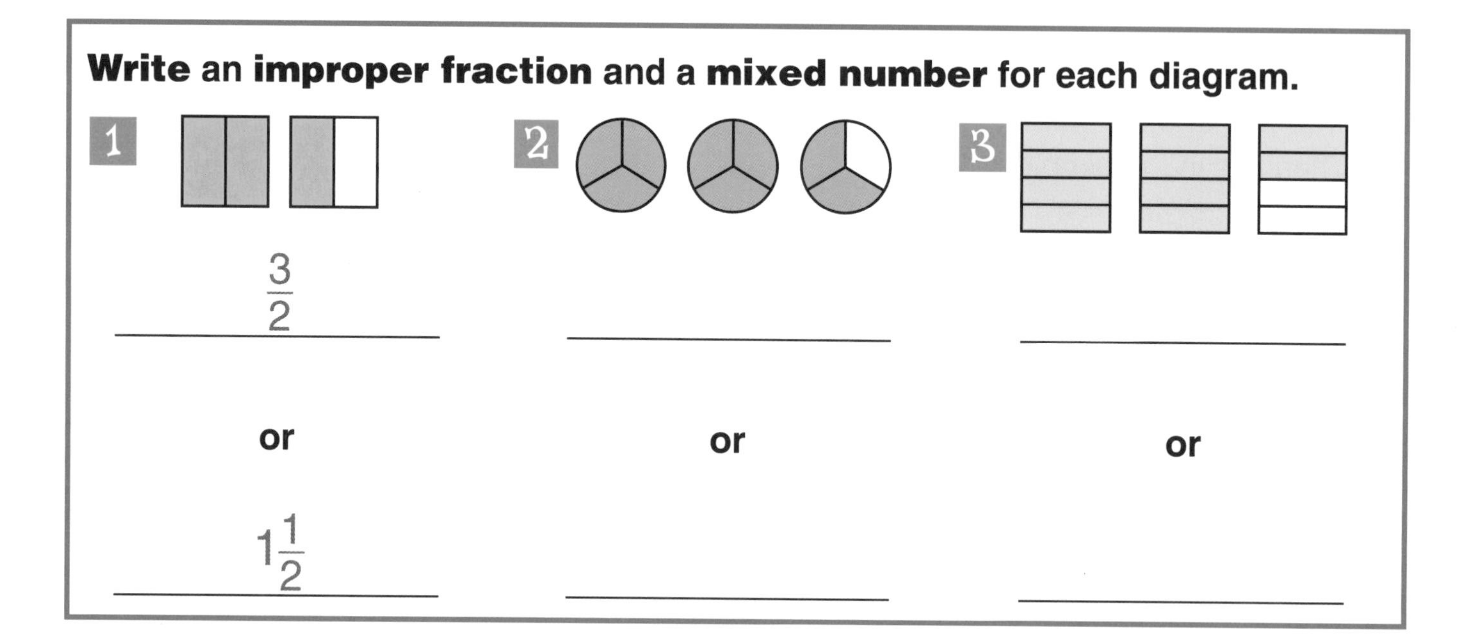

Write an improper fraction and a mixed number for each diagram.
1
2
3
3/2
or
or
or
1 1/2


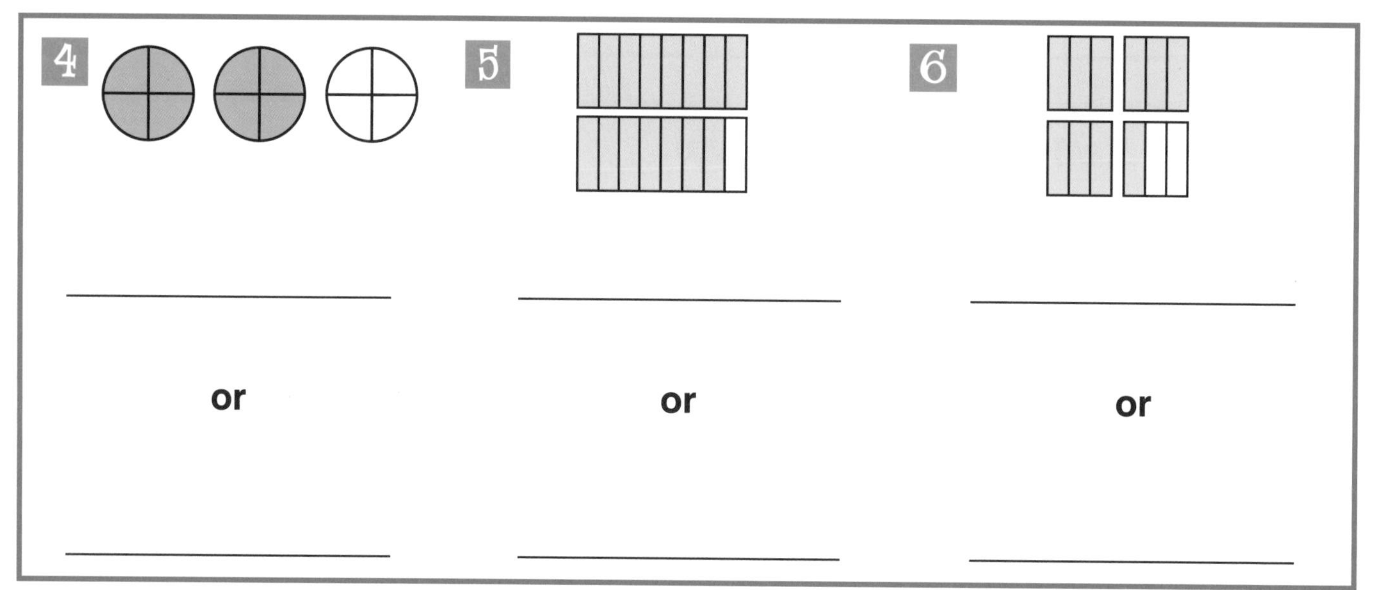

# Improper Fractions

**You can change a mixed number into an improper fraction.**

1. Multiply the whole number by the denominator.
2. Add the numerator.
3. Set that numerator over the original denominator.

**EXAMPLE** Change $3\frac{2}{3}$ into an improper fraction.

- Multiply $3 \times 3$. ( 9 )
- Add 2. ( $9 + 2 = 11$ )
- Set 11 over the original denominator. ( $\frac{11}{3}$ )

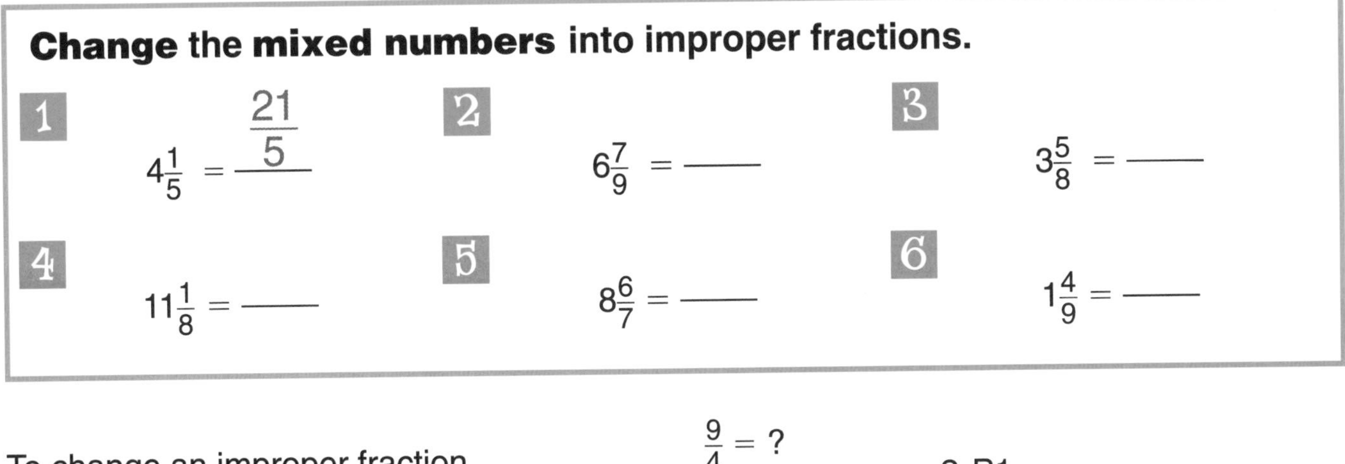

**Change the mixed numbers into improper fractions.**

1. $4\frac{1}{5} = \frac{21}{5}$
2. $6\frac{7}{9} =$ ____
3. $3\frac{5}{8} =$ ____
4. $11\frac{1}{8} =$ ____
5. $8\frac{6}{7} =$ ____
6. $1\frac{4}{9} =$ ____

To change an improper fraction to a whole or a mixed number:

1. Divide the numerator by the denominator to get the whole number.
2. If there is a remainder, set the remainder over the divisor to get the fraction.

$\frac{9}{4} = ?$

$$\begin{array}{r} 2 \text{ R1} \\ 4\overline{)9} \\ -\underline{8} \\ 1 \end{array}$$

$\frac{1}{4}$ (Remainder) (Divisor) $\quad \frac{9}{4} = 2\frac{1}{4}$

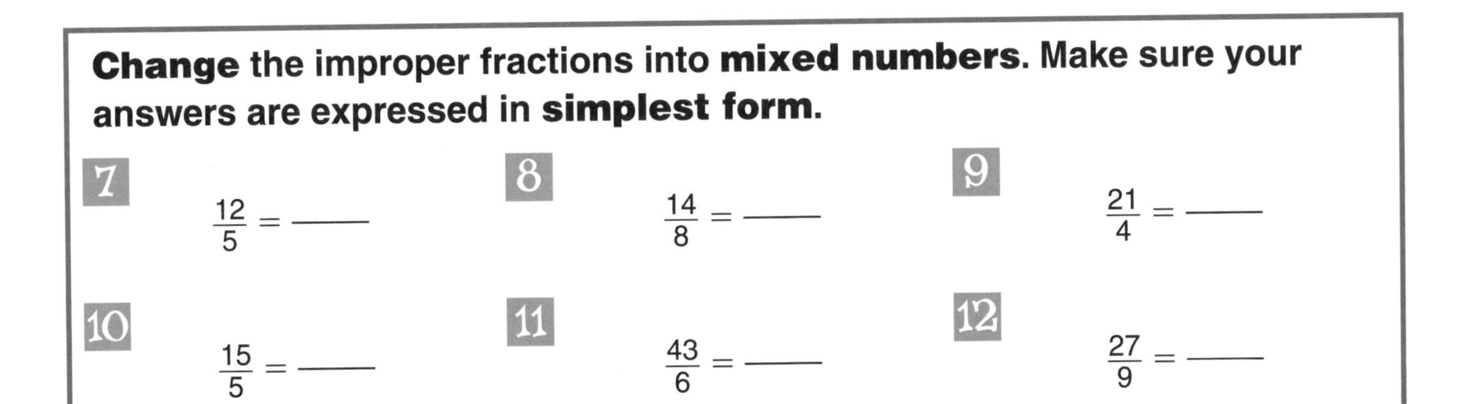

**Change** the improper fractions into **mixed numbers.** Make sure your answers are expressed in **simplest form.**

7. $\frac{12}{5} =$ ____
8. $\frac{14}{8} =$ ____
9. $\frac{21}{4} =$ ____
10. $\frac{15}{5} =$ ____
11. $\frac{43}{6} =$ ____
12. $\frac{27}{9} =$ ____

# Add and Subtract Fractions

When adding or subtracting fractions with the same denominator, ONLY add or subtract the numerators. Keep the denominator the same. Make sure to express your answer in simplest form.

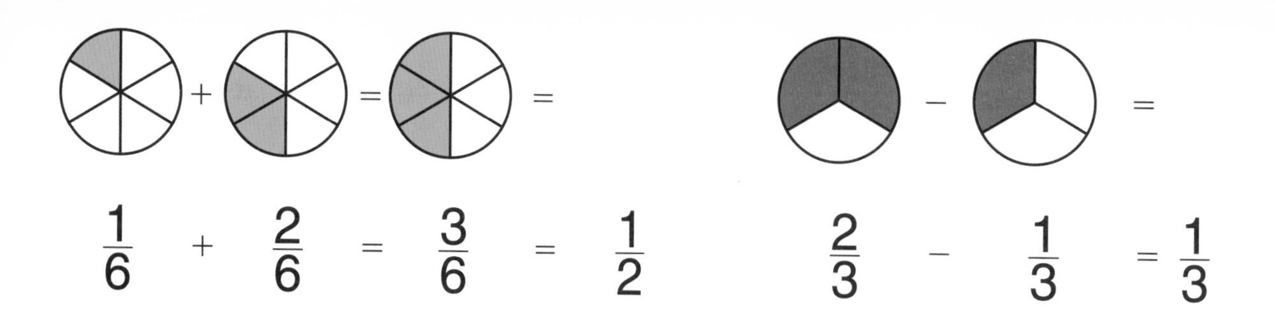

$\frac{1}{6} + \frac{2}{6} = \frac{3}{6} = \frac{1}{2}$      $\frac{2}{3} - \frac{1}{3} = \frac{1}{3}$

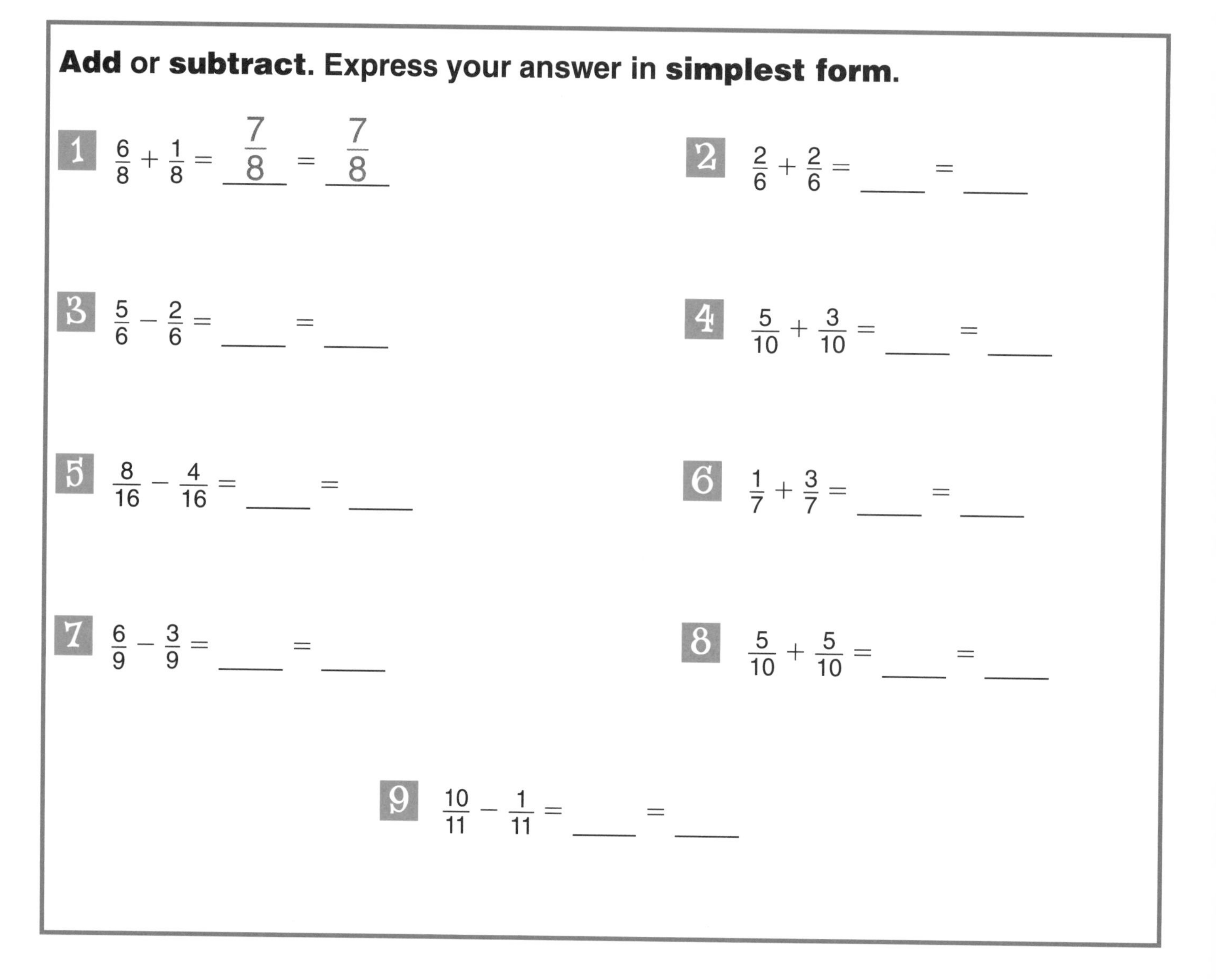

**Add or subtract**. Express your answer in **simplest form.**

1. $\frac{6}{8} + \frac{1}{8} = \frac{7}{8} = \frac{7}{8}$
2. $\frac{2}{6} + \frac{2}{6} =$ ____ = ____
3. $\frac{5}{6} - \frac{2}{6} =$ ____ = ____
4. $\frac{5}{10} + \frac{3}{10} =$ ____ = ____
5. $\frac{8}{16} - \frac{4}{16} =$ ____ = ____
6. $\frac{1}{7} + \frac{3}{7} =$ ____ = ____
7. $\frac{6}{9} - \frac{3}{9} =$ ____ = ____
8. $\frac{5}{10} + \frac{5}{10} =$ ____ = ____
9. $\frac{10}{11} - \frac{1}{11} =$ ____ = ____

# Add Fractions

**When adding fractions with unlike denominators, find an equivalent fraction or fractions with a common denominator**

To find a common denominator think of a number that can be divided by both 2 and 3.

$$\frac{1}{2} + \frac{1}{3} = ?$$

$$\frac{1 \times 3}{2 \times 3} = \frac{3}{6}$$

$$\frac{1 \times 2}{3 \times 2} = \frac{2}{6}$$

Add fractions with the same denominators, by adding the numerators and keeping the denominator the same.

$$\frac{3}{6} + \frac{2}{6} = \frac{5}{6}$$

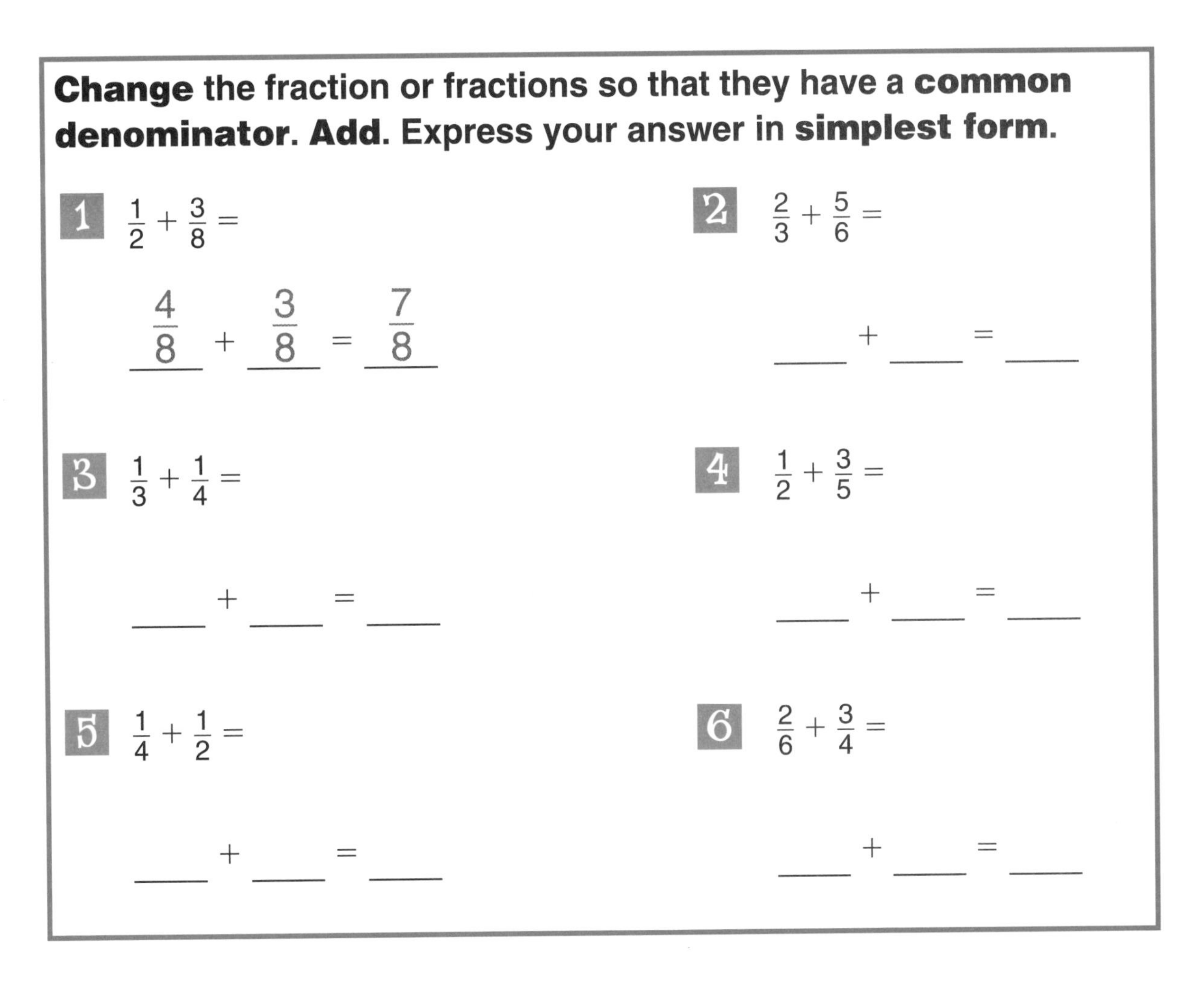

**Change** the fraction or fractions so that they have a **common denominator. Add.** Express your answer in **simplest form.**

1. $\frac{1}{2} + \frac{3}{8} =$

   $\frac{4}{8} + \frac{3}{8} = \frac{7}{8}$

2. $\frac{2}{3} + \frac{5}{6} =$

   ____ + ____ = ____

3. $\frac{1}{3} + \frac{1}{4} =$

   ____ + ____ = ____

4. $\frac{1}{2} + \frac{3}{5} =$

   ____ + ____ = ____

5. $\frac{1}{4} + \frac{1}{2} =$

   ____ + ____ = ____

6. $\frac{2}{6} + \frac{3}{4} =$

   ____ + ____ = ____

# Subtract Fractions

Here's how to subtract fractions with unlike denominators.

**1.** Convert one or both fractions to share a common denominator.

$\frac{1}{4} - \frac{1}{12} =$ The common denominator is 12.

**2.** Subtract.

**3.** Simplify. You only need to change one fraction.

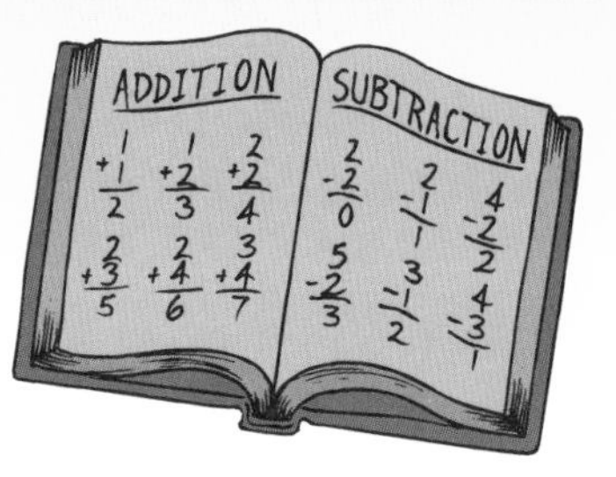


$$\frac{1 \times 3}{4 \times 3} = \frac{3}{12} - \frac{1}{12} = \frac{2 \div 2}{12 \div 2} = \frac{1}{6}$$ **is** in simplest form.

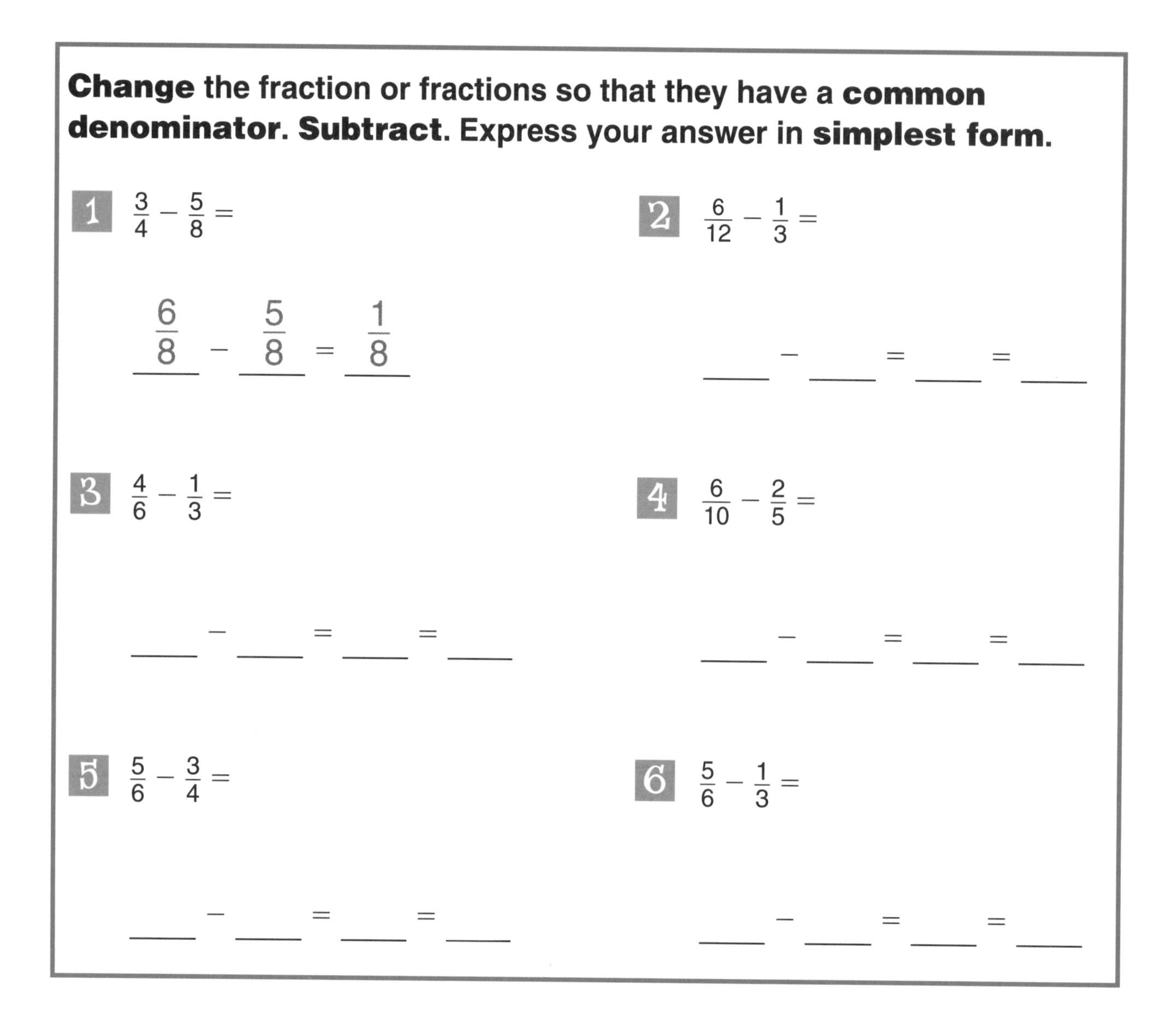

**Change** the fraction or fractions so that they have a **common denominator. Subtract.** Express your answer in **simplest form.**

**1** $\frac{3}{4} - \frac{5}{8} =$

$\frac{6}{8} - \frac{5}{8} = \frac{1}{8}$

**2** $\frac{6}{12} - \frac{1}{3} =$

____ − ____ = ____ = ____

**3** $\frac{4}{6} - \frac{1}{3} =$

____ − ____ = ____ = ____

**4** $\frac{6}{10} - \frac{2}{5} =$

____ − ____ = ____ = ____

**5** $\frac{5}{6} - \frac{3}{4} =$

____ − ____ = ____ = ____

**6** $\frac{5}{6} - \frac{1}{3} =$

____ − ____ = ____ = ____

# Relate Fractions to Decimals

Like a fraction, a decimal shows part of a whole number. With decimals, the whole is always broken into ten or a power of ten.

The fraction $\frac{8}{10}$ looks like

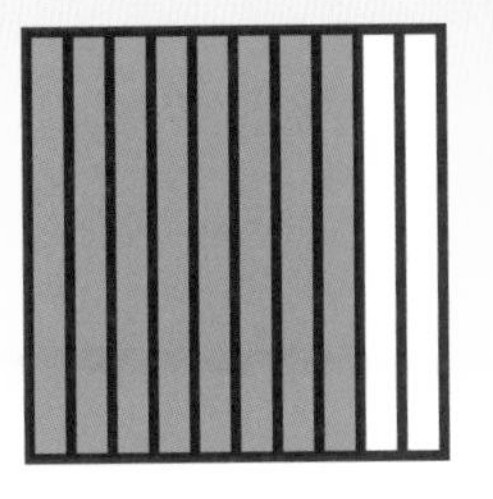

It can also be written as .8

The fraction $\frac{8}{100}$ looks like

It can also be written as .08

**Write a fraction and a decimal for each model. The first one is done for you.**

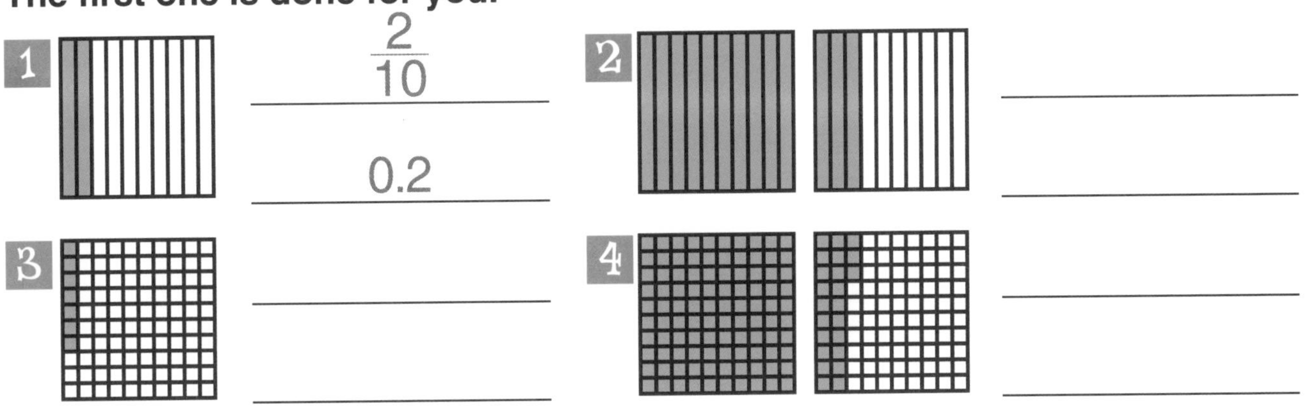

1. $\frac{2}{10}$ — 0.2
2. ________ ________
3. ________ ________
4. ________ ________

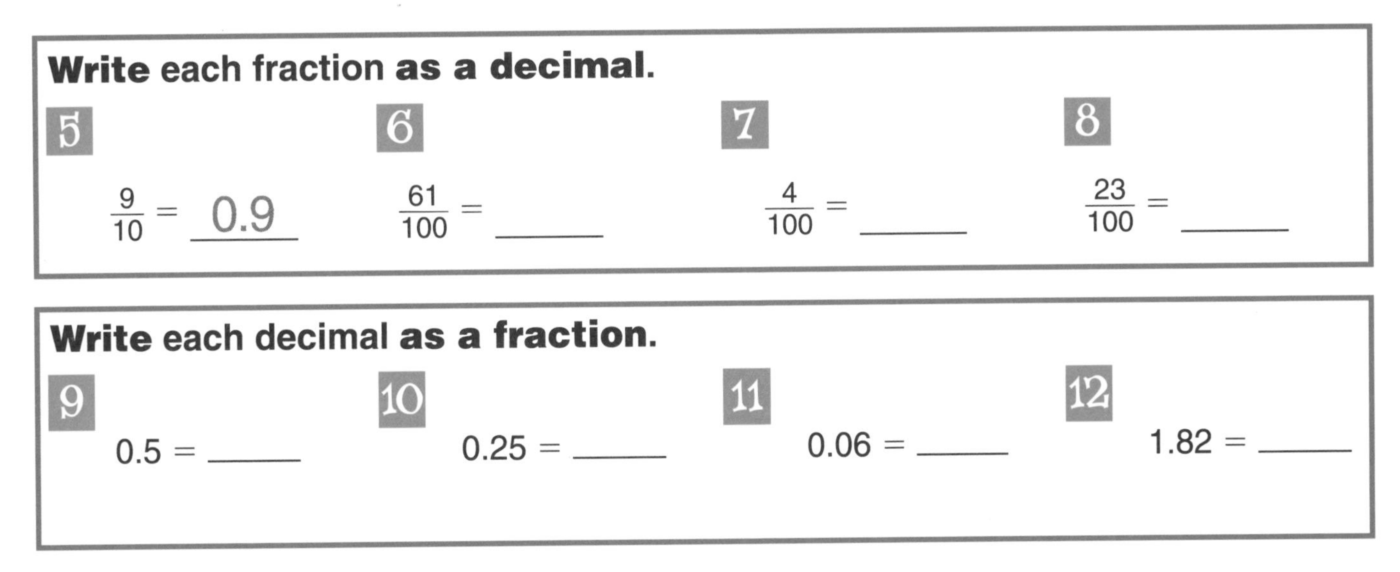

**Write each fraction as a decimal.**

5. $\frac{9}{10} =$ 0.9
6. $\frac{61}{100} =$ ______
7. $\frac{4}{100} =$ ______
8. $\frac{23}{100} =$ ______

**Write each decimal as a fraction.**

9. 0.5 = ______
10. 0.25 = ______
11. 0.06 = ______
12. 1.82 = ______

# Adding and Subtracting Decimals

When adding or subtracting decimals follow these steps.

1. Line up decimal points.
2. Add **zeros** as needed.
3. Add or subtract while regrouping if needed.

**EXAMPLE**

Add 2.4, 6.78, and 5

$$\begin{array}{r} \overset{1}{2}.40 \\ 6.78 \\ +\ 5.00 \\ \hline 14.18 \end{array}$$

Subtract 6.2 − 1.38

$$\begin{array}{r} 6.20 \\ -\ 1.38 \\ \hline 4.82 \end{array}$$

**Add** or **subtract**. **Pay attention to the signs.**

1. $\begin{array}{r} \overset{8}{\cancel{9}}.\overset{1}{2} \\ -\ 7.5 \\ \hline 1.7 \end{array}$

2. $\begin{array}{r} 29.91 \\ +\ 30.77 \\ \hline \end{array}$

3. $\begin{array}{r} 0.70 \\ +0.32 \\ \hline \end{array}$

4. $\begin{array}{r} 4.57 \\ -\ 3.90 \\ \hline \end{array}$

5. $\begin{array}{r} 17.2 \\ +\ 8.6 \\ \hline \end{array}$

6. $\begin{array}{r} 5.25 \\ -\ 2.70 \\ \hline \end{array}$

7. $\begin{array}{r} 4.60 \\ 4.06 \\ +\ 46.00 \\ \hline \end{array}$

8. $\begin{array}{r} 8.50 \\ -\ 3.99 \\ \hline \end{array}$

**Add** or **subtract**. **Pay attention to the signs.**

9. 7.06 + 8

=

10. 7.03 − 1.6

=

11. 7.3 + 73

=

12. 26 − 2.6

=

# Compare and Order Decimals

When comparing decimals follow these steps.

1. Line up the decimal points. — 1.**4**6
2. Find the first place where the digits are different. — 1.**6** is the same as 1.60.
3. Compare. — **6 > 4 so 1.6 > 1.46**

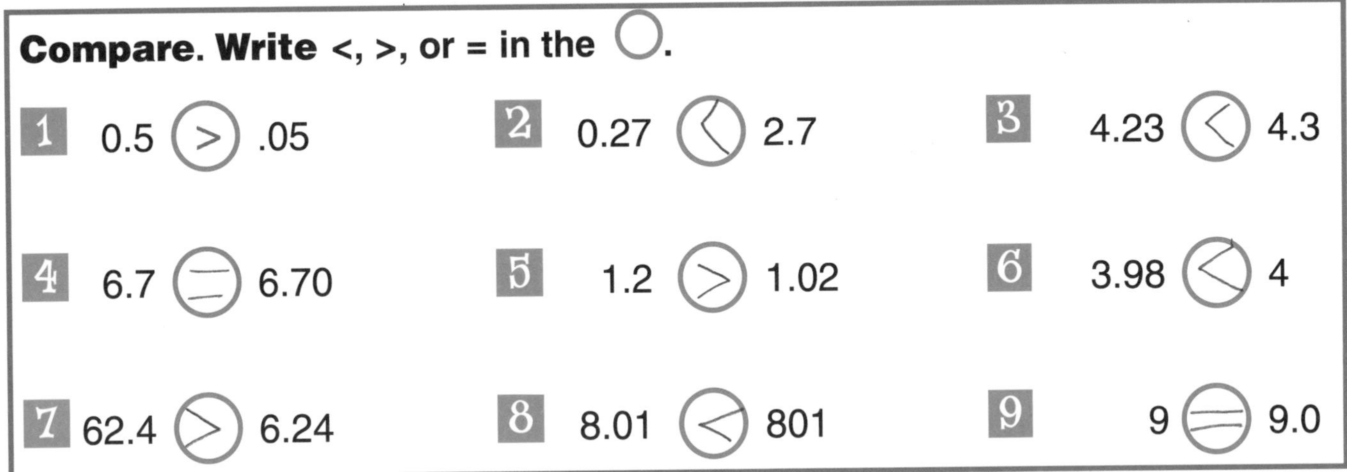

**Compare. Write <, >, or = in the ○.**

1. 0.5 ○ .05 (>)
2. 0.27 ○ 2.7 (<)
3. 4.23 ○ 4.3 (<)
4. 6.7 ○ 6.70 (=)
5. 1.2 ○ 1.02 (>)
6. 3.98 ○ 4 (<)
7. 62.4 ○ 6.24 (>)
8. 8.01 ○ 801 (<)
9. 9 ○ 9.0 (=)

**Order the numbers from least to greatest.**

10. 0.04 4.0 0.4 0.44 — 0.04, 0.4, 0.44, 4.0
11. 0.63 6.3 6.03 3.6 ______
12. 3.2 $3\frac{4}{10}$ 3.33 $3\frac{1}{100}$ ______
13. 6.8 9.6 8.6 6.9 ______

# Rounding Decimals

To round the decimal **24.6** to the nearest **whole number**, first **underline** the entire whole number. If the digit to the **right** of that number is 5 or higher, increase the whole number by one and leave off the decimal. If the digit to the **right** of that number is less than 5, keep the whole number the same and leave off the decimal.

24.6 Underline the 24. Look at the 6. Since 6 is greater than 5, change the 24 to 25 and leave off the decimal.

24.6 rounded to the nearest whole number is 25.

To round the decimal **8.31** to the nearest **tenth**, first underline the digit in the tenths place. Look at the digit to the right of that number (the hundredths place). If it is 5 or higher, increase the underlined digit by one and leave off the rest of the decimal. If it is less than 5, keep the underlined digit the same and leave off the rest of the decimal.

8.43 Underline the 4. Look at the 3. Since 3 is less than 5, keep the 4 the same and leave off the rest of the decimal.

8.43 rounded to the nearest tenth is 8.4.

**Round** each decimal to the **nearest whole number.**

1. 67.8 68
2. 16.05 ____
3. 63.47 ____
4. 37.68 ____
5. 47.85 ____
6. 123.4 ____
7. 9.41 ____
8. 9.76 ____

**Round** each decimal to the **nearest tenth.**

9. 74.54 74.5
10. 82.17 ____
11. 5.56 ____
12. 32.73 ____
13. 3.89 ____
14. 5.64 ____
15. 68.37 ____
16. 6.86 ____

# Math Review

You have done a terrific job. Now it is time to see how much you actually know!

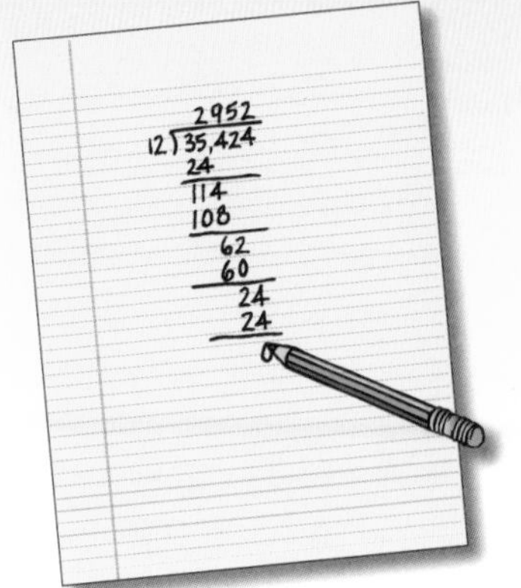

**Tips for answering multiple choice questions:**

1. Always read the question carefully.
2. Get rid of any choices you know are definitely not right.
3. Even if you think that you have found the right answer, check all other choices to make sure they cannot be correct.

**CIRCLE the letter of the correct answer. Use a separate sheet of paper to work out each problem.**

**1** Four million, sixteen thousand, two hundred thirty-six in **standard form** is:

A. 40,16, 236
B. 4,160,236
C. 4,016,236
D. 4,16,000,236

**2** The **word name** for 27,008,054 is:

A. twenty-seven thousand, eight hundred fifty-four
B. twenty-seven million, eight thousand fifty-four
C. twenty-seven million, eighty-thousand
D. two million, seven hundred and eight thousand, fifty-four

**3** In what place is the 0 in 43,078,234?

A. thousands
B. millions
C. hundred thousands
D. ten thousands

**4** Which set of numbers is ordered from **greatest to least?**

A. 70,007 77,700 77,707
B. 77,777 70,700 70,007
C. 70,007 70,700 77,777
D. 77,777 70,007 70,700

**5** 402,758 to the nearest **thousand** is:

A. 402,800
B. 502,758
C. 403,758
D. 403,000

**6** A good estimate for 684 + 2,317 is:

A. 3,001
B. 2,700
C. 3,000
D. 3,700

**7** 6,754 + 24,598 =
A. 31,532
B. 30,352
C. 31,352
D. 31,252

**8** 706 − 89 =
A. 627
B. 618
C. 613
D. 617

**9** A good estimate for 78 × 534 is:
A. 4,000
B. 40,000
C. 400,000
D. 41,652

**10** 653 × 76 =
A. 49,828
B. 8,489
C. 49,628
D. 48,628

**11** 85 divided by 9 is:
A. 9 R4
B. 9
C. 9 R5
D. 10

**12** If 702 is the dividend, and 6 is the divisor, what is the **quotient**?
A. 107
B. 117
C. 116 R6
D. 177

**13** The **product** of 504 and 8 is:
A. 512
B. 4,032
C. 4,112
D. 4,036

**14** $\frac{5}{8} + \frac{3}{8} =$
A. $\frac{8}{16}$
B. $\frac{1}{2}$
C. 1
D. $\frac{7}{8}$

**15** Which set of decimals is ordered from least to greatest?
A. 8.6 6.8 0.86 0.68
B. 8.6 6.8 0.86 0.68
C. 68 0.86 6.8 8.6
D. 0.68 0.86 6.8 8.6

**16** 6.8 − 2.59 =
A. 4.29
B. 42.1
C. 4.21
D. 4.12

# Answer Key

## Place Value through the Millions

Did you know that lightning strikes about 259,200,000 times per month on our planet?

**word name:** two hundred fifty-nine million, two hundred thousand
**standard form:** 259,200,000
**expanded form:** 200,000,000 + 50,000,000 + 9,000,000 + 200,000

**Write each number in standard form and expanded form.**

1 seven million, two hundred four thousand, five hundred thirty-two

7,204,532 and 7, 000,000 + 200,000 + 4,000 + 532

2 eighty-two million, one hundred seventeen thousand, eleven

82,117,011 and 82,000,000 + 117,000 + 11

**Place Value**

These are the place values for 643,927,860.

| one hundred million | ten million | million | one hundred thousand | ten thousand | one thousand | one hundred | ten | one |
|---|---|---|---|---|---|---|---|---|
| 6 | 4 | 3 | 9 | 2 | 7 | 8 | 6 | 0 |

**Write the name of the place value of the number in bold.**

EXAMPLE 7**4**6,208,015 ten million

4 78, 3**4**2, 807 ten thousand

5 **4**26, 786, 035 hundred million

6 623, **4**09, 672 hundred thousand



## Compare and Order Numbers

To compare numbers you start from the highest place value. Find the first place where the digits are different. Then compare those digits.

Compare 72,415 and 73,872

7**2**,415 7**3**,872

< means **less than**
> means **greater than**
= means **equals**

**A crocodile facing left means greater than.**

2 thousand < 3 thousand so 72,415 < 73,872

**Compare** the numbers. Write <, >, or = in the circle.

1 113,406 (>) 111,897

2 472,654 (<) 475,862

3 fifteen thousand twenty (=) 15,020

4 70,090 (=) seventy thousand ninety

5 54 + 10 (<) 63 + 5

6 116 + 4 (=) 124 – 4

**Order** the numbers from **least** to **greatest**.

7 22,000 220,000 202,000 20,022

20,022; 22,000; 202,000; 220,000

8 17,707 717,077 77,117 71,770

17,707; 71,770; 77,117; 717,077

**Write** the number.

9 Write the number that is two less than 6,789. 6,787

10 Write the number that is ten more than 72,567. 72,577



## Rounding Numbers

To round a number to the hundreds place first **underline** the hundreds place.

If the digit to the **right** of that number is **5 or higher**, increase the underlined digit by one and change the rest of the numbers on the right to zeros.

If the digit to the **right** of that number is **less than 5**, keep the underlined digit the same and change the rest of the numbers on the right to zeros.

Round **68,462** to the nearest hundred.

68,462 Underline the 4. Look at the 6. Since 6 is greater than 5, change the 4 to a 5 and change the rest of the numbers on the right to zeros.

68,462 rounded to the nearest hundred is 68,**500**

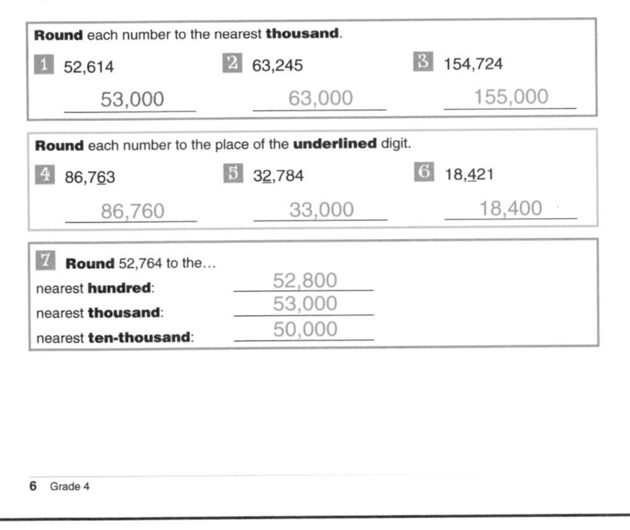

**Round** each number to the nearest **thousand**.

1 52,614 — 53,000

2 63,245 — 63,000

3 154,724 — 155,000

**Round** each number to the place of the **underlined** digit.

4 86,763 — 86,760

5 32,784 — 33,000

6 18,421 — 18,400

7 **Round** 52,764 to the…

nearest **hundred**: 52,800
nearest **thousand**: 53,000
nearest **ten-thousand**: 50,000



## Rounding and Estimation

Before adding, round each addend to its highest place value. Add those numbers to get an **estimate**. Check the actual **sum** against your **estimate** to see if it makes sense.

4,9 2 3 → rounds to 5,000
+ 7 8 4 → rounds to + 800
5,7 0 7 → estimate: 5,800

actual sum: **5,707**

Since the actual sum is close to the estimate, the answer makes sense.

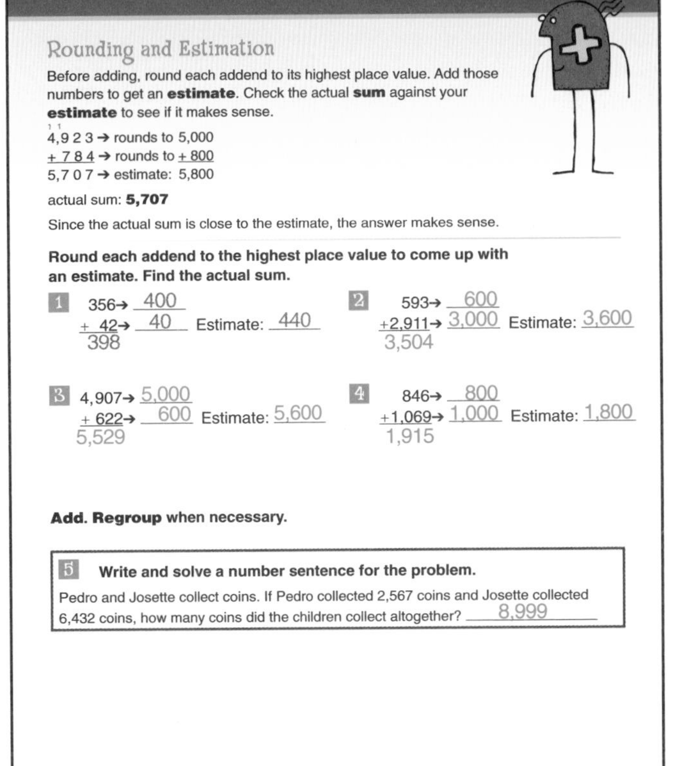

**Round each addend to the highest place value to come up with an estimate. Find the actual sum.**

1 356 → 400; + 42 → 40; 398 Estimate: 440

2 593 → 600; +2,911 → 3,000; 3,504 Estimate: 3,600

3 4,907 → 5,000; + 622 → 600; 5,529 Estimate: 5,600

4 846 → 800; +1,069 → 1,000; 1,915 Estimate: 1,800

**Add. Regroup** when necessary.

5 **Write and solve a number sentence for the problem.**

Pedro and Josette collect coins. If Pedro collected 2,567 coins and Josette collected 6,432 coins, how many coins did the children collect altogether? 8,999

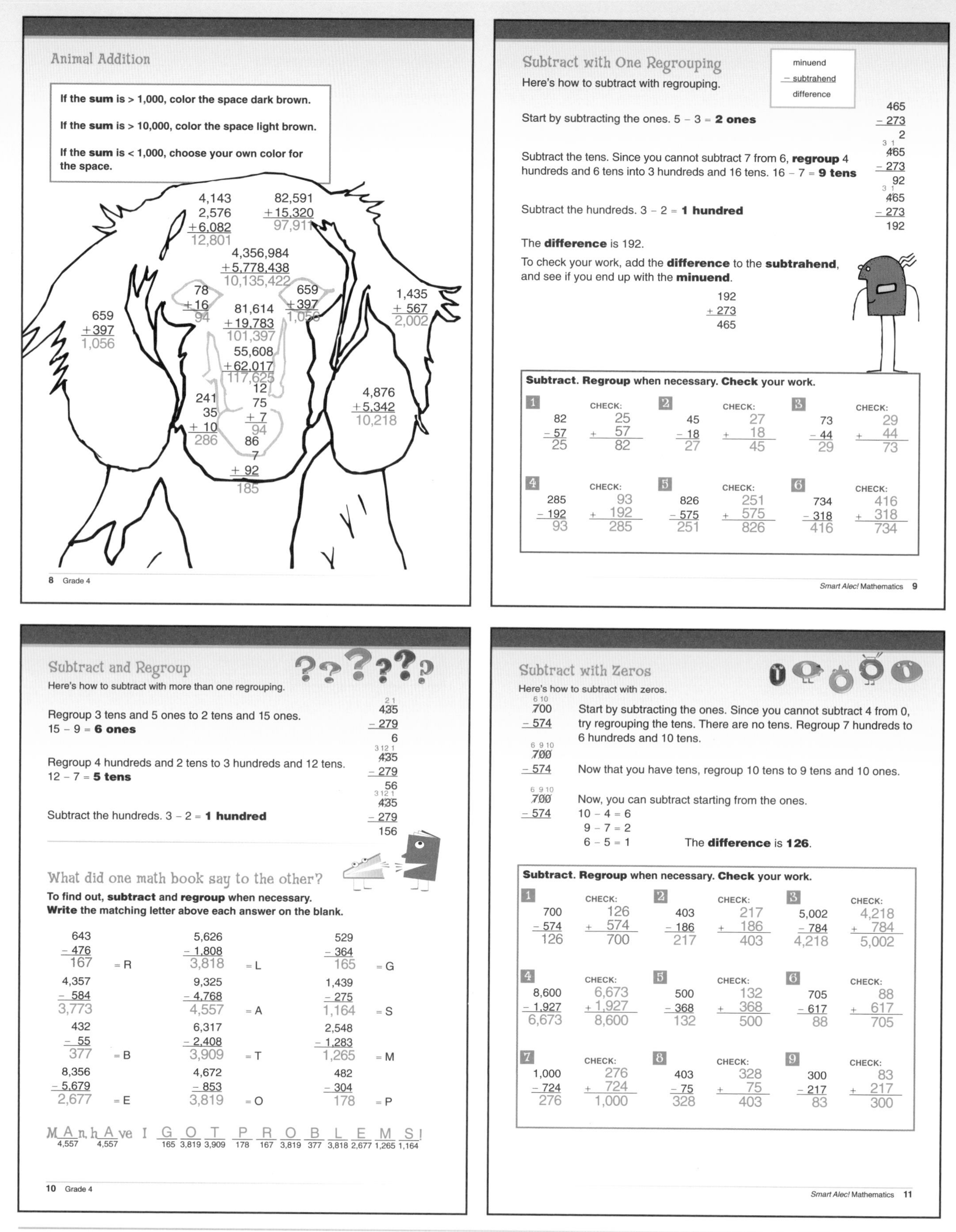

## Animal Addition

If the **sum** is > 1,000, color the space dark brown.

If the **sum** is > 10,000, color the space light brown.

If the **sum** is < 1,000, choose your own color for the space.

4,143 + 2,576 + 6,082 = 12,801

82,591 + 15,320 = 97,911

4,356,984 + 5,778,438 = 10,135,422

78 + 16 = 94

659 + 397 = 1,056

1,435 + 567 = 2,002

659 + 397 = 1,056

81,614 + 19,783 = 101,397

55,608 + 62,017 = 117,625

12 + 75 + 7 = 94

241 + 35 + 10 = 286

4,876 + 5,342 = 10,218

86 + 7 + 92 = 185

8 Grade 4

## Subtract with One Regrouping

Here's how to subtract with regrouping.

minuend
– subtrahend
difference

Start by subtracting the ones. 5 – 3 = **2 ones**

465 – 273 = 2

Subtract the tens. Since you cannot subtract 7 from 6, **regroup** 4 hundreds and 6 tens into 3 hundreds and 16 tens. 16 – 7 = **9 tens**

465 – 273 = 92

Subtract the hundreds. 3 – 2 = **1 hundred**

465 – 273 = 192

The **difference** is 192.

To check your work, add the **difference** to the **subtrahend**, and see if you end up with the **minuend**.

192 + 273 = 465

**Subtract. Regroup** when necessary. **Check** your work.

1. 82 – 57 = 25; CHECK: 25 + 57 = 82
2. 45 – 18 = 27; CHECK: 27 + 18 = 45
3. 73 – 44 = 29; CHECK: 29 + 44 = 73
4. 285 – 192 = 93; CHECK: 93 + 192 = 285
5. 826 – 575 = 251; CHECK: 251 + 575 = 826
6. 734 – 318 = 416; CHECK: 416 + 318 = 734

*Smart Alec!* Mathematics 9

## Subtract and Regroup

Here's how to subtract with more than one regrouping.

Regroup 3 tens and 5 ones to 2 tens and 15 ones. 15 – 9 = **6 ones**

435 – 279 = 6

Regroup 4 hundreds and 2 tens to 3 hundreds and 12 tens. 12 – 7 = **5 tens**

435 – 279 = 56

Subtract the hundreds. 3 – 2 = **1 hundred**

435 – 279 = 156

### What did one math book say to the other?

To find out, **subtract** and **regroup** when necessary. **Write** the matching letter above each answer on the blank.

643 – 476 = 167 = R
5,626 – 1,808 = 3,818 = L
529 – 364 = 165 = G
4,357 – 584 = 3,773
9,325 – 4,768 = 4,557 = A
1,439 – 275 = 1,164 = S
432 – 55 = 377 = B
6,317 – 2,408 = 3,909 = T
2,548 – 1,283 = 1,265 = M
8,356 – 5,679 = 2,677 = E
4,672 – 853 = 3,819 = O
482 – 304 = 178 = P

M A n h A ve I G O T P R O B L E M S!

4,557 4,557 165 3,819 3,909 178 167 3,819 377 3,818 2,677 1,265 1,164

10 Grade 4

## Subtract with Zeros

Here's how to subtract with zeros.

700 – 574: Start by subtracting the ones. Since you cannot subtract 4 from 0, try regrouping the tens. There are no tens. Regroup 7 hundreds to 6 hundreds and 10 tens.

700 – 574: Now that you have tens, regroup 10 tens to 9 tens and 10 ones.

700 – 574: Now, you can subtract starting from the ones.
10 – 4 = 6
9 – 7 = 2
6 – 5 = 1

The **difference** is **126**.

**Subtract. Regroup** when necessary. **Check** your work.

1. 700 – 574 = 126; CHECK: 126 + 574 = 700
2. 403 – 186 = 217; CHECK: 217 + 186 = 403
3. 5,002 – 784 = 4,218; CHECK: 4,218 + 784 = 5,002
4. 8,600 – 1,927 = 6,673; CHECK: 6,673 + 1,927 = 8,600
5. 500 – 368 = 132; CHECK: 132 + 368 = 500
6. 705 – 617 = 88; CHECK: 88 + 617 = 705
7. 1,000 – 724 = 276; CHECK: 276 + 724 = 1,000
8. 403 – 75 = 328; CHECK: 328 + 75 = 403
9. 300 – 217 = 83; CHECK: 83 + 217 = 300

*Smart Alec!* Mathematics 11

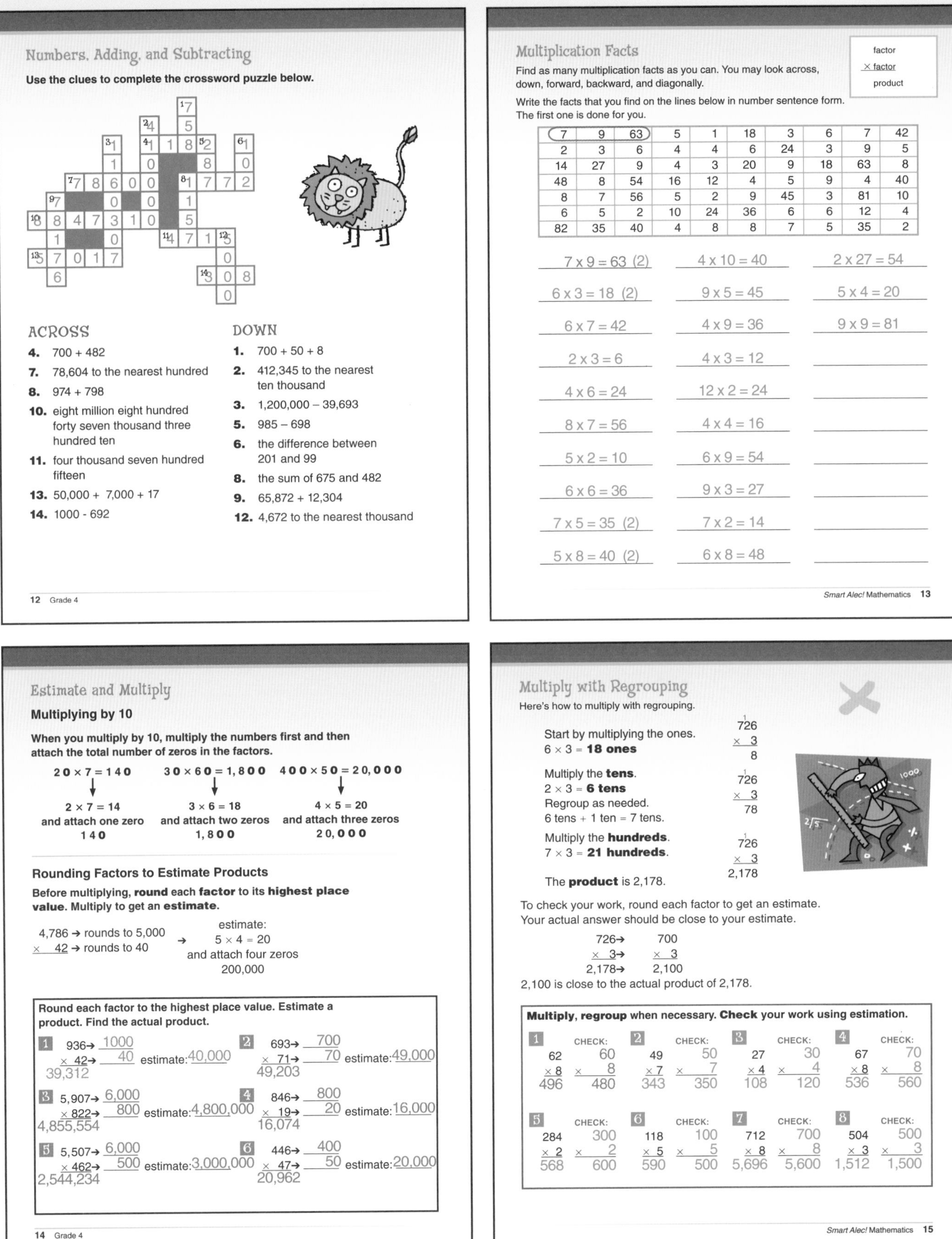

## Numbers, Adding, and Subtracting

**Use the clues to complete the crossword puzzle below.**

### ACROSS

**4.** 700 + 482
**7.** 78,604 to the nearest hundred
**8.** 974 + 798
**10.** eight million eight hundred forty seven thousand three hundred ten
**11.** four thousand seven hundred fifteen
**13.** 50,000 + 7,000 + 17
**14.** 1000 - 692

### DOWN

**1.** 700 + 50 + 8
**2.** 412,345 to the nearest ten thousand
**3.** 1,200,000 – 39,693
**5.** 985 – 698
**6.** the difference between 201 and 99
**8.** the sum of 675 and 482
**9.** 65,872 + 12,304
**12.** 4,672 to the nearest thousand

12 Grade 4

## Multiplication Facts

Find as many multiplication facts as you can. You may look across, down, forward, backward, and diagonally.

factor
× factor
product

Write the facts that you find on the lines below in number sentence form. The first one is done for you.

| | | | | | | | | | |
|---|---|---|---|---|---|---|---|---|---|
| 7 | 9 | 63 | 5 | 1 | 18 | 3 | 6 | 7 | 42 |
| 2 | 3 | 6 | 4 | 4 | 6 | 24 | 3 | 9 | 5 |
| 14 | 27 | 9 | 4 | 3 | 20 | 9 | 18 | 63 | 8 |
| 48 | 8 | 54 | 16 | 12 | 4 | 5 | 9 | 4 | 40 |
| 8 | 7 | 56 | 5 | 2 | 9 | 45 | 3 | 81 | 10 |
| 6 | 5 | 2 | 10 | 24 | 36 | 6 | 6 | 12 | 4 |
| 82 | 35 | 40 | 4 | 8 | 8 | 7 | 5 | 35 | 2 |

7 x 9 = 63 (2)
6 x 3 = 18 (2)
6 x 7 = 42
2 x 3 = 6
4 x 6 = 24
8 x 7 = 56
5 x 2 = 10
6 x 6 = 36
7 x 5 = 35 (2)
5 x 8 = 40 (2)
4 x 10 = 40
9 x 5 = 45
4 x 9 = 36
4 x 3 = 12
12 x 2 = 24
4 x 4 = 16
6 x 9 = 54
9 x 3 = 27
7 x 2 = 14
6 x 8 = 48
2 x 27 = 54
5 x 4 = 20
9 x 9 = 81

*Smart Alec!* Mathematics 13

## Estimate and Multiply

### Multiplying by 10

**When you multiply by 10, multiply the numbers first and then attach the total number of zeros in the factors.**

**20 × 7 = 140** → 2 × 7 = 14 and attach one zero **140**

**30 × 60 = 1,800** → 3 × 6 = 18 and attach two zeros **1,800**

**400 × 50 = 20,000** → 4 × 5 = 20 and attach three zeros **20,000**

### Rounding Factors to Estimate Products

**Before multiplying, round each factor to its highest place value. Multiply to get an estimate.**

4,786 → rounds to 5,000
× 42 → rounds to 40
→ estimate: 5 × 4 = 20 and attach four zeros 200,000

**Round each factor to the highest place value. Estimate a product. Find the actual product.**

1. 936 → 1000; × 42 → 40; estimate: 40,000; 39,312
2. 693 → 700; × 71 → 70; estimate: 49,000; 49,203
3. 5,907 → 6,000; × 822 → 800; estimate: 4,800,000; 4,855,554
4. 846 → 800; × 19 → 20; estimate: 16,000; 16,074
5. 5,507 → 6,000; × 462 → 500; estimate: 3,000,000; 2,544,234
6. 446 → 400; × 47 → 50; estimate: 20,000; 20,962

14 Grade 4

## Multiply with Regrouping

Here's how to multiply with regrouping.

Start by multiplying the ones.
6 × 3 = **18 ones**
726 × 3 = 8

Multiply the **tens**.
2 × 3 = **6 tens**
Regroup as needed.
6 tens + 1 ten = 7 tens.
726 × 3 = 78

Multiply the **hundreds**.
7 × 3 = **21 hundreds**.
726 × 3 = 2,178

The **product** is 2,178.

To check your work, round each factor to get an estimate. Your actual answer should be close to your estimate.

726 → 700
× 3 → × 3
2,178 → 2,100

2,100 is close to the actual product of 2,178.

**Multiply, regroup** when necessary. **Check** your work using estimation.

1. 62 × 8 = 496; CHECK: 60 × 8 = 480
2. 49 × 7 = 343; CHECK: 50 × 7 = 350
3. 27 × 4 = 108; CHECK: 30 × 4 = 120
4. 67 × 8 = 536; CHECK: 70 × 8 = 560
5. 284 × 2 = 568; CHECK: 300 × 2 = 600
6. 118 × 5 = 590; CHECK: 100 × 5 = 500
7. 712 × 8 = 5,696; CHECK: 700 × 8 = 5,600
8. 504 × 3 = 1,512; CHECK: 500 × 3 = 1,500

*Smart Alec!* Mathematics 15

## Multiplying Two Digit Numbers

Multiply each digit in the top factor by the ones of the **bottom factor**.
87 × 3 = **261** by the ones of the bottom factor.

```
  2
  87
× 43
 261
```

Place a zero in the ones column as a place holder.

```
  87
× 43
 261
   0
```

Multiply each digit in the top factor by the tens of the **bottom factor**.
87 × 4 = **348**

Add the numbers.
261 + 3,480 = **3,741**

```
    87
  × 43
   261
+3,480
 3,741
```

**Find the product.** Remember to line up your numbers carefully.

| | | | |
|---|---|---|---|
| 1. 54 × 32 = 1,728 | 2. 46 × 28 = 1,288 | 3. 507 × 84 = 42,588 | 4. 667 × 94 = 62,698 |
| 5. 43 × 16 = 688 | 6. 52 × 34 = 1,768 | 7. 465 × 17 = 7,905 | 8. 643 × 78 = 50,154 |

16 Grade 4

## Multiply Two Digit Numbers

What is it?
It appears once in a minute, twice in a week, and once in a year.

To find out, **multiply. Write** the matching letter on the blank space above the answers at the bottom of the page.

| | | |
|---|---|---|
| 289 × 76 = 21,964 | 25 × 68 = 1,700 =H | 39 × 75 = 2,925 |
| 683 × 19 = 12,977 | 200 × 70 = 14,000 =R | 548 × 63 = 34,524 =T |
| 629 × 8 = 5,032 =L | 529 × 64 = 33,856 | 482 × 91 = 43,862 =E |

| T | H | E | L | E | T | T | E | R | "E" |
|---|---|---|---|---|---|---|---|---|---|
| 34,524 | 1,700 | 43,862 | 5,032 | 43,862 | 34,524 | 34,524 | 43,862 | 14,000 | 43,862 |

*Smart Alec!* Mathematics 17

## Estimate and Divide

Here's how to use division facts you know to estimate a quotient.

To estimate a quotient, think of a division fact you know. **34 ÷ 8**

QUOTIENT
DIVISOR )DIVIDEND

OR

32 ÷ 8 = 4. The fact is close, but not too large. **34 ÷ 8 is about 4.**

DIVIDEND ÷ DIVISOR = QUOTIENT

**Estimate** the quotient. **Write** the division fact you know under each problem.

1. 65 ÷ 8 is about 8. — 64 ÷ 8 = 8
2. 75 ÷ 8 is about 9. — 72 ÷ 8 = 9
3. 36 ÷ 5 is about 7. — 35 ÷ 5 = 7
4. 49 ÷ 6 is about 8. — 48 ÷ 6 = 8
5. 65 ÷ 9 is about 7. — 63 ÷ 9 = 7
6. 19 ÷ 3 is about 6. — 18 ÷ 3 = 6
7. 33 ÷ 8 is about 4. — 32 ÷ 8 = 4
8. 37 ÷ 6 is about 6. — 36 ÷ 6 = 6

18 Grade 4

## Division with Remainders

**Often, one number can not be evenly divided by another number. In this case, there are leftovers. In math, we call the leftovers a remainder.**

**XAMPLE** The clown divides **25** balloons among **4** children. Each child gets **6** balloons. There is **1** balloon leftover.

| Divide | Multiply | Subtract | Remainder |
|---|---|---|---|
| 6)25 → 4 | 6)25 → 4, 24 | 6)25 → 4, − 24, 1 | The number 1 can not be divided by 6. The 1 is left over and becomes a remainder. The quotient is 4 R1. |

To check, multiply the quotient by the divisor. Then, add the remainder. Your answer should be the dividend.

```
 4 quotient
×6 divisor
24
+1 remainder
25 dividend
```

**Divide. Check your answer.**

1. 3)20 = 6 R2 — CHECK: 6 × 3 = 18, + 2 = 20
2. 7)52 = 7 R3 — CHECK: 7 × 7 = 49, + 3 = 52
3. 5)42 = 8 R2 — CHECK: 8 × 5 = 40, + 2 = 42
4. 6)39 = 6 R3 — CHECK: 6 × 6 = 36, + 3 = 39
5. 4)38 = 9 R2 — CHECK: 9 × 4 = 36, + 2 = 38
6. 8)75 = 9 R3 — CHECK: 9 × 8 = 72, + 3 = 75

*Smart Alec!* Mathematics 19

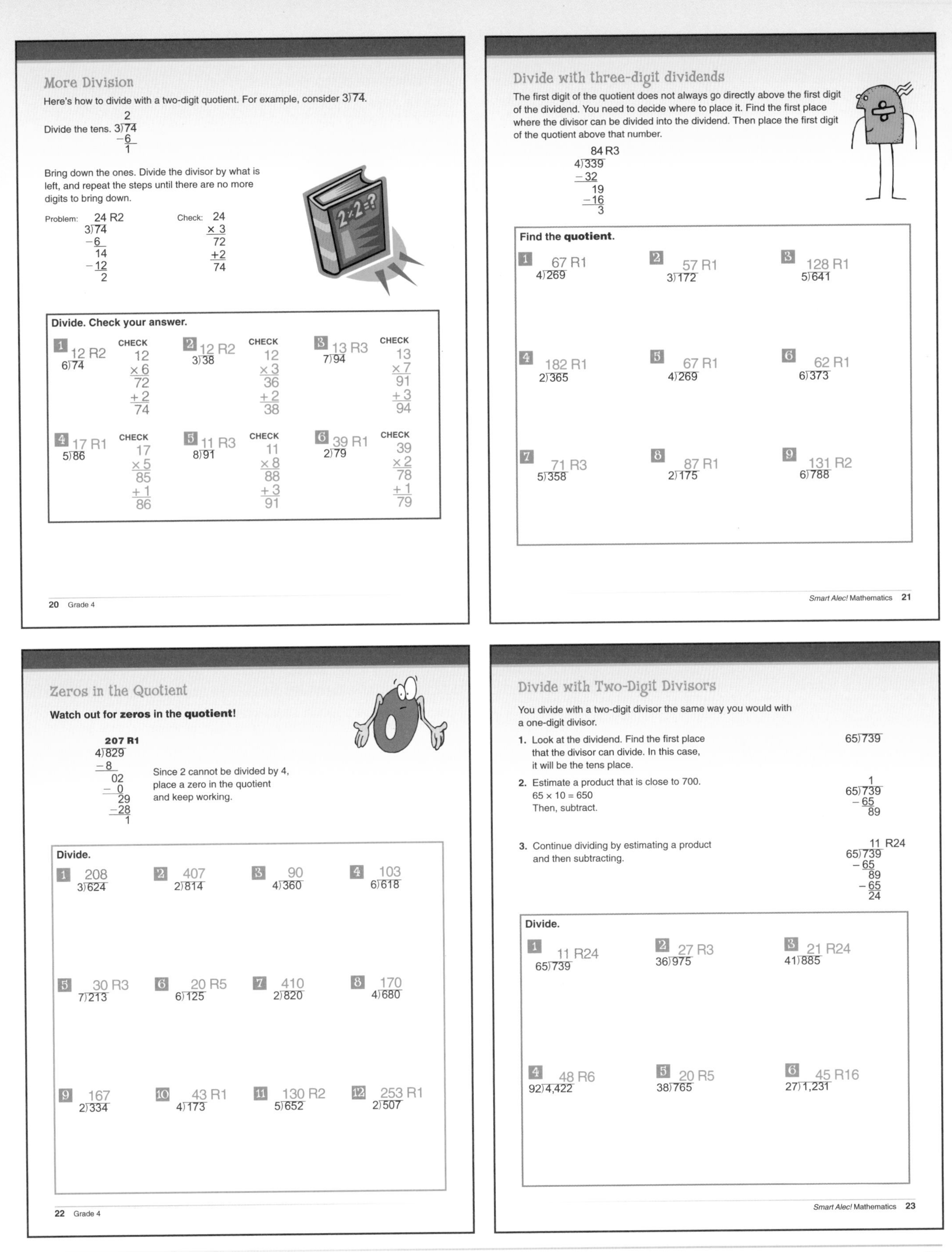

## More Division

Here's how to divide with a two-digit quotient. For example, consider 3)74.

Divide the tens.

```
   2
3)74
 -6
  1
```

Bring down the ones. Divide the divisor by what is left, and repeat the steps until there are no more digits to bring down.

```
Problem:  24 R2      Check:  24
         3)74                x 3
          -6                  72
           14                 +2
          -12                 74
            2
```

**Divide. Check your answer.**

1. 6)74 — 12 R2; CHECK: 12 × 6 = 72, + 2 = 74
2. 3)38 — 12 R2; CHECK: 12 × 3 = 36, + 2 = 38
3. 7)94 — 13 R3; CHECK: 13 × 7 = 91, + 3 = 94
4. 5)86 — 17 R1; CHECK: 17 × 5 = 85, + 1 = 86
5. 8)91 — 11 R3; CHECK: 11 × 8 = 88, + 3 = 91
6. 2)79 — 39 R1; CHECK: 39 × 2 = 78, + 1 = 79

20 Grade 4

## Divide with three-digit dividends

The first digit of the quotient does not always go directly above the first digit of the dividend. You need to decide where to place it. Find the first place where the divisor can be divided into the dividend. Then place the first digit of the quotient above that number.

```
  84 R3
4)339
 -32
   19
  -16
    3
```

Find the **quotient.**

1. 4)269 — 67 R1
2. 3)172 — 57 R1
3. 5)641 — 128 R1
4. 2)365 — 182 R1
5. 4)269 — 67 R1
6. 6)373 — 62 R1
7. 5)358 — 71 R3
8. 2)175 — 87 R1
9. 6)788 — 131 R2

*Smart Alec!* Mathematics 21

## Zeros in the Quotient

**Watch out for zeros in the quotient!**

```
  207 R1
4)829
 -8
  02
 - 0
   29
  -28
    1
```

Since 2 cannot be divided by 4, place a zero in the quotient and keep working.

**Divide.**

1. 3)624 — 208
2. 2)814 — 407
3. 4)360 — 90
4. 6)618 — 103
5. 7)213 — 30 R3
6. 6)125 — 20 R5
7. 2)820 — 410
8. 4)680 — 170
9. 2)334 — 167
10. 4)173 — 43 R1
11. 5)652 — 130 R2
12. 2)507 — 253 R1

22 Grade 4

## Divide with Two-Digit Divisors

You divide with a two-digit divisor the same way you would with a one-digit divisor.

1. Look at the dividend. Find the first place that the divisor can divide. In this case, it will be the tens place. — 65)739
2. Estimate a product that is close to 700. 65 × 10 = 650. Then, subtract.

```
   1
65)739
  -65
   89
```

3. Continue dividing by estimating a product and then subtracting.

```
   11 R24
65)739
  -65
   89
  -65
   24
```

**Divide.**

1. 65)739 — 11 R24
2. 36)975 — 27 R3
3. 41)885 — 21 R24
4. 92)4,422 — 48 R6
5. 38)765 — 20 R5
6. 27)1,231 — 45 R16

*Smart Alec!* Mathematics 23

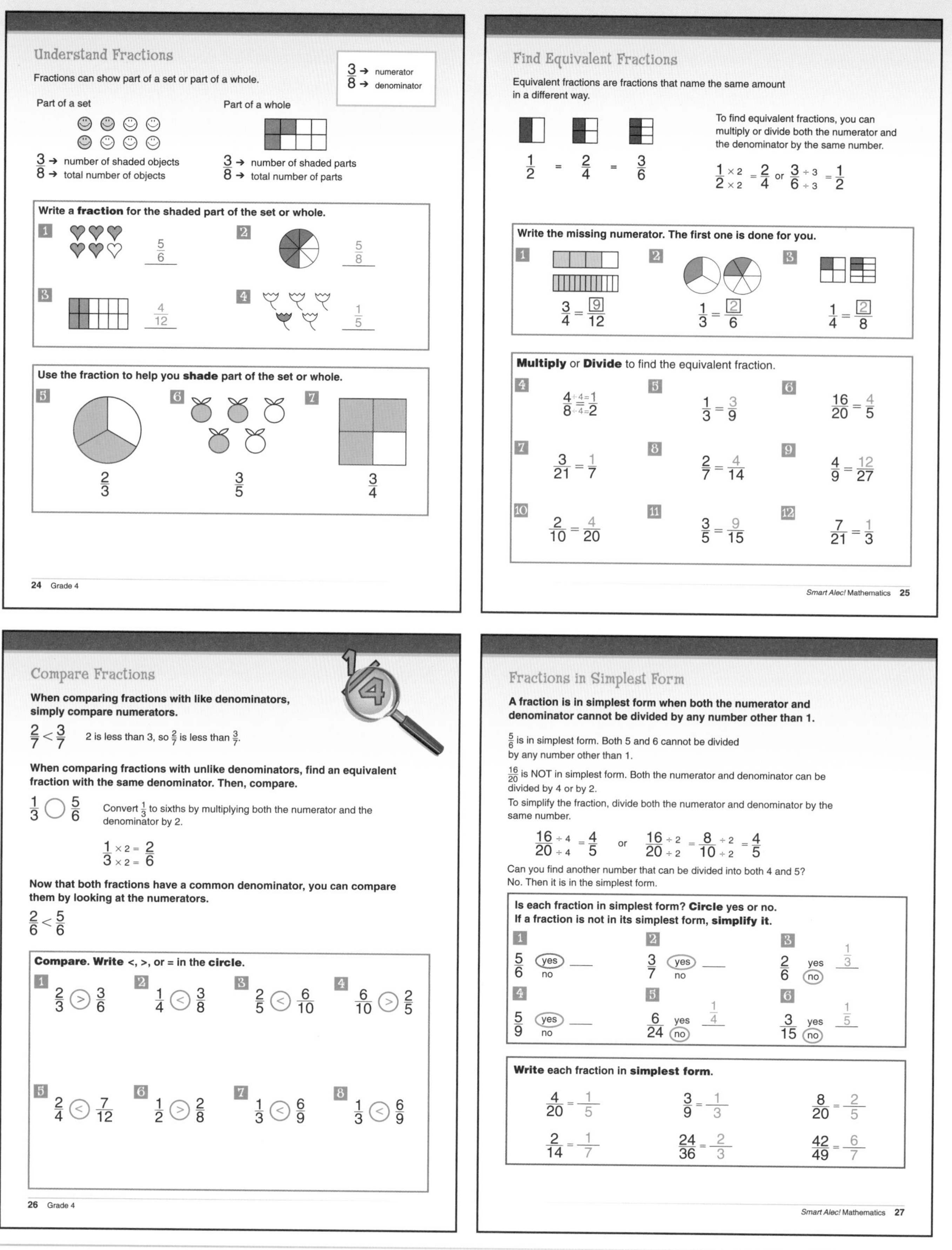

## Understand Fractions

Fractions can show part of a set or part of a whole.

3 → numerator
8 → denominator

Part of a set

3 → number of shaded objects
8 → total number of objects

Part of a whole

3 → number of shaded parts
8 → total number of parts

**Write a fraction for the shaded part of the set or whole.**

1 $\frac{5}{6}$ 2 $\frac{5}{8}$

3 $\frac{4}{12}$ 4 $\frac{1}{5}$

**Use the fraction to help you shade part of the set or whole.**

5 $\frac{2}{3}$ 6 $\frac{3}{5}$ 7 $\frac{3}{4}$

24 Grade 4

## Find Equivalent Fractions

Equivalent fractions are fractions that name the same amount in a different way.

$\frac{1}{2} = \frac{2}{4} = \frac{3}{6}$

To find equivalent fractions, you can multiply or divide both the numerator and the denominator by the same number.

$\frac{1 \times 2}{2 \times 2} = \frac{2}{4}$ or $\frac{3 \div 3}{6 \div 3} = \frac{1}{2}$

**Write the missing numerator. The first one is done for you.**

1 $\frac{3}{4} = \frac{9}{12}$ 2 $\frac{1}{3} = \frac{2}{6}$ 3 $\frac{1}{4} = \frac{2}{8}$

**Multiply** or **Divide** to find the equivalent fraction.

4 $\frac{4 \div 4}{8 \div 4} = \frac{1}{2}$ 5 $\frac{1}{3} = \frac{3}{9}$ 6 $\frac{16}{20} = \frac{4}{5}$

7 $\frac{3}{21} = \frac{1}{7}$ 8 $\frac{2}{7} = \frac{4}{14}$ 9 $\frac{4}{9} = \frac{12}{27}$

10 $\frac{2}{10} = \frac{4}{20}$ 11 $\frac{3}{5} = \frac{9}{15}$ 12 $\frac{7}{21} = \frac{1}{3}$

*Smart Alec!* Mathematics 25

## Compare Fractions

**When comparing fractions with like denominators, simply compare numerators.**

$\frac{2}{7} < \frac{3}{7}$ 2 is less than 3, so $\frac{2}{7}$ is less than $\frac{3}{7}$.

**When comparing fractions with unlike denominators, find an equivalent fraction with the same denominator. Then, compare.**

$\frac{1}{3}$ ◯ $\frac{5}{6}$ Convert $\frac{1}{3}$ to sixths by multiplying both the numerator and the denominator by 2.

$\frac{1 \times 2}{3 \times 2} = \frac{2}{6}$

**Now that both fractions have a common denominator, you can compare them by looking at the numerators.**

$\frac{2}{6} < \frac{5}{6}$

**Compare. Write <, >, or = in the circle.**

1 $\frac{2}{3} > \frac{3}{6}$ 2 $\frac{1}{4} < \frac{3}{8}$ 3 $\frac{2}{5} < \frac{6}{10}$ 4 $\frac{6}{10} > \frac{2}{5}$

5 $\frac{2}{4} < \frac{7}{12}$ 6 $\frac{1}{2} > \frac{2}{8}$ 7 $\frac{1}{3} < \frac{6}{9}$ 8 $\frac{1}{3} < \frac{6}{9}$

26 Grade 4

## Fractions in Simplest Form

**A fraction is in simplest form when both the numerator and denominator cannot be divided by any number other than 1.**

$\frac{5}{6}$ is in simplest form. Both 5 and 6 cannot be divided by any number other than 1.

$\frac{16}{20}$ is NOT in simplest form. Both the numerator and denominator can be divided by 4 or by 2.

To simplify the fraction, divide both the numerator and denominator by the same number.

$\frac{16 \div 4}{20 \div 4} = \frac{4}{5}$ or $\frac{16 \div 2}{20 \div 2} = \frac{8 \div 2}{10 \div 2} = \frac{4}{5}$

Can you find another number that can be divided into both 4 and 5? No. Then it is in the simplest form.

**Is each fraction in simplest form? Circle yes or no. If a fraction is not in its simplest form, simplify it.**

1 $\frac{5}{6}$ (yes) no ___ 2 $\frac{3}{7}$ (yes) no ___ 3 $\frac{2}{6}$ yes (no) $\frac{1}{3}$

4 $\frac{5}{9}$ (yes) no ___ 5 $\frac{6}{24}$ yes (no) $\frac{1}{4}$ 6 $\frac{3}{15}$ yes (no) $\frac{1}{5}$

**Write each fraction in simplest form.**

$\frac{4}{20} = \frac{1}{5}$ $\frac{3}{9} = \frac{1}{3}$ $\frac{8}{20} = \frac{2}{5}$

$\frac{2}{14} = \frac{1}{7}$ $\frac{24}{36} = \frac{2}{3}$ $\frac{42}{49} = \frac{6}{7}$

*Smart Alec!* Mathematics 27

## Mixed Numbers

A mixed number is a whole number with a fraction.

$2\frac{1}{2}, 1\frac{3}{4}, 5\frac{4}{7}$

An improper fraction is a fraction whose numerator is larger than its denominator.

$\frac{8}{7}, \frac{20}{9}, \frac{11}{2}$

Notice how this picture can be seen as $\frac{5}{4}$ (improper) or $1\frac{1}{4}$ (a mixed number).

**Write** an **improper fraction** and a **mixed number** for each diagram.

1. $\frac{3}{2}$ or $1\frac{1}{2}$
2. $\frac{8}{3}$ or $2\frac{2}{3}$
3. $\frac{10}{4}$ or $2\frac{1}{2}$
4. $\frac{8}{4}$ or $2$
5. $\frac{15}{8}$ or $1\frac{7}{8}$
6. $\frac{10}{3}$ or $3\frac{1}{3}$



## Improper Fractions

**You can change a mixed number into an improper fraction.**

1. Multiply the whole number by the denominator.
2. Add the numerator.
3. Set that numerator over the original denominator.

EXAMPLE Change $3\frac{2}{3}$ into an improper fraction.

- Multiply 3 × 3. ( 9 )
- Add 2. ( 9 + 2 = 11 )
- Set 11 over the original denominator. ( $\frac{11}{3}$ )

**Change** the **mixed numbers** into improper fractions.

1. $4\frac{1}{5} = \frac{21}{5}$
2. $6\frac{7}{9} = \frac{61}{9}$
3. $3\frac{5}{8} = \frac{29}{8}$
4. $11\frac{1}{8} = \frac{89}{8}$
5. $8\frac{6}{7} = \frac{62}{7}$
6. $1\frac{4}{9} = \frac{13}{9}$

To change an improper fraction to a whole or a mixed number:

1. Divide the numerator by the denominator to get the whole number.
2. If there is a remainder, set the remainder over the divisor to get the fraction.

$\frac{9}{4} = ?$

$9 \div 4 = 2$ R1 ($9 - 8 = 1$)

$\frac{1}{4}$ (Remainder)/(Divisor) $\frac{9}{4} = 2\frac{1}{4}$

**Change** the improper fractions into **mixed numbers**. Make sure your answers are expressed in **simplest form.**

7. $\frac{12}{5} = 2\frac{2}{5}$
8. $\frac{14}{8} = 1\frac{3}{4}$
9. $\frac{21}{4} = 5\frac{1}{4}$
10. $\frac{15}{5} = 3$
11. $\frac{43}{6} = 7\frac{1}{6}$
12. $\frac{27}{9} = 3$



## Add and Subtract Fractions

When adding or subtracting fractions with the same denominator, ONLY add or subtract the numerators. Keep the denominator the same. Make sure to express your answer in simplest form.

$\frac{1}{6} + \frac{2}{6} = \frac{3}{6} = \frac{1}{2}$

$\frac{2}{3} - \frac{1}{3} = \frac{1}{3}$

**Add or subtract.** Express your answer in **simplest form.**

1. $\frac{6}{8} + \frac{1}{8} = \frac{7}{8} = \frac{7}{8}$
2. $\frac{2}{6} + \frac{2}{6} = \frac{4}{6} = \frac{2}{3}$
3. $\frac{5}{6} - \frac{2}{6} = \frac{3}{6} = \frac{1}{2}$
4. $\frac{5}{10} + \frac{3}{10} = \frac{8}{10} = \frac{4}{5}$
5. $\frac{8}{16} - \frac{4}{16} = \frac{4}{16} = \frac{1}{4}$
6. $\frac{1}{7} + \frac{3}{7} = \frac{4}{7} = \frac{4}{7}$
7. $\frac{6}{9} - \frac{3}{9} = \frac{3}{9} = \frac{1}{3}$
8. $\frac{5}{10} + \frac{5}{10} = \frac{10}{10} = 1$
9. $\frac{10}{11} - \frac{1}{11} = \frac{9}{11} = \frac{9}{11}$



## Add Fractions

**When adding fractions with unlike denominators, find an equivalent fraction or fractions with a common denominator**

To find a common denominator think of a number that can be divided by both 2 and 3.

$\frac{1}{2} + \frac{1}{3} = ?$

$\frac{1 \times 3}{2 \times 3} = \frac{3}{6}$

$\frac{1 \times 2}{3 \times 2} = \frac{2}{6}$

Add fractions with the same denominators, by adding the numerators and keeping the denominator the same.

$\frac{3}{6} + \frac{2}{6} = \frac{5}{6}$

**Change** the fraction or fractions so that they have a **common denominator. Add.** Express your answer in **simplest form.**

1. $\frac{1}{2} + \frac{3}{8} =$ $\frac{4}{8} + \frac{3}{8} = \frac{7}{8}$
2. $\frac{2}{3} + \frac{5}{6} =$ $\frac{4}{6} + \frac{5}{6} = \frac{3}{2}$
3. $\frac{1}{3} + \frac{1}{4} =$ $\frac{4}{12} + \frac{3}{12} = \frac{7}{12}$
4. $\frac{1}{2} + \frac{3}{5} =$ $\frac{5}{10} + \frac{6}{10} = \frac{11}{10}$
5. $\frac{1}{4} + \frac{1}{2} =$ $\frac{1}{4} + \frac{2}{4} = \frac{3}{4}$
6. $\frac{2}{6} + \frac{3}{4} =$ $\frac{4}{12} + \frac{9}{12} = \frac{13}{12}$

## Subtract Fractions

Here's how to subtract fractions with unlike denominators.

1. Convert one or both fractions to share a common denominator.

$\frac{1}{4} - \frac{1}{12} =$ The common denominator is 12.

2. Subtract.
3. Simplify.

You only need to change one fraction.

ADDITION SUBTRACTION

$\frac{1 \times 3}{4 \times 3} = \frac{3}{12} - \frac{1}{12} = \frac{2 \div 2}{12 \div 2} = \frac{1}{6}$ is in simplest form.

**Change** the fraction or fractions so that they have a **common denominator. Subtract.** Express your answer in **simplest form.**

1. $\frac{3}{4} - \frac{5}{8} =$ $\frac{6}{8} - \frac{5}{8} = \frac{1}{8}$
2. $\frac{6}{12} - \frac{1}{3} =$ $\frac{6}{12} - \frac{4}{12} = \frac{2}{12} = \frac{1}{6}$
3. $\frac{4}{6} - \frac{1}{3} =$ $\frac{4}{6} - \frac{2}{6} = \frac{2}{6} = \frac{1}{3}$
4. $\frac{6}{10} - \frac{2}{5} =$ $\frac{6}{10} - \frac{4}{10} = \frac{2}{10} = \frac{1}{5}$
5. $\frac{5}{6} - \frac{3}{4} =$ $\frac{10}{12} - \frac{9}{12} = \frac{1}{12} = \frac{1}{12}$
6. $\frac{5}{6} - \frac{1}{3} =$ $\frac{5}{6} - \frac{2}{6} = \frac{3}{6} = \frac{1}{2}$



## Relate Fractions to Decimals

Like a fraction, a decimal shows part of a whole number. With decimals, the whole is always broken into ten or a power of ten.

The fraction $\frac{8}{10}$ looks like

It can also be written as .8

The fraction $\frac{8}{100}$ looks like

It can also be written as .08

**Write** a **fraction** and a **decimal** for each model. The first one is done for you.

1. $\frac{2}{10}$ 0.2
2. $\frac{13}{10}$ 1.3
3. $\frac{7}{100}$ 0.07
4. $\frac{123}{100}$ 1.23

**Write** each fraction **as a decimal.**

5. $\frac{9}{10} =$ 0.9
6. $\frac{61}{100} =$ 0.61
7. $\frac{4}{100} =$ 0.04
8. $\frac{23}{100} =$ 0.23

**Write** each decimal **as a fraction.**

9. 0.5 = $\frac{1}{2}$
10. 0.25 = $\frac{1}{4}$
11. 0.06 = $\frac{3}{50}$
12. 1.82 = $\frac{91}{50}$



## Adding and Subtracting Decimals

When adding or subtracting decimals follow these steps.

1. Line up decimal points.
2. Add **zeros** as needed.
3. Add or subtract while regrouping if needed.

**XAMPLE**

Add 2.4, 6.78, and 5

```
  2.40
  6.78
+ 5.00
 14.18
```

Subtract 6.2 − 1.38

```
  6.20
− 1.38
  4.82
```

**Add** or **subtract.** Pay attention to the signs.

1. 9.2 − 7.5 = 1.7
2. 29.91 + 30.77 = 60.68
3. 0.70 + 0.32 = 1.02
4. 4.57 − 3.90 = 0.67
5. 17.2 + 8.6 = 25.8
6. 5.25 − 2.70 = 2.55
7. 4.60 + 4.06 + 46.00 = 54.66
8. 8.50 − 3.99 = 4.51

**Add** or **subtract.** Pay attention to the signs.

9. 7.06 + 8 = 15.06
10. 7.03 − 1.6 = 5.43
11. 7.3 + 73 = 80.3
12. 26 − 2.6 = 23.4



## Compare and Order Decimals

When comparing decimals follow these steps.

1. Line up the decimal points. — 1.**4**6
2. Find the first place where the digits are different. — 1.**6** is the same as 1.60.
3. Compare. — **6 > 4 so 1.6 > 1.46**

**Compare. Write** <, >, or = in the ○.

1. 0.5 (>) .05
2. 0.27 (<) 2.7
3. 4.23 (<) 4.3
4. 6.7 (=) 6.70
5. 1.2 (>) 1.02
6. 3.98 (<) 4
7. 62.4 (>) 6.24
8. 8.01 (<) 801
9. 9 (=) 9.0

**Order the numbers from least to greatest.**

10. 0.04 4.0 0.4 0.44 — 0.04, 0.4, 0.44, 4.0
11. 0.63 6.3 6.03 3.6 — 0.63, 3.6, 6.03, 6.3
12. 3.2 $3\frac{4}{10}$ 3.33 $3\frac{1}{100}$ — $3\frac{1}{100}$, 3.2, 3.33, $3\frac{4}{10}$
13. 6.8 9.6 8.6 6.9 — 6.8, 6.9, 8.6, 9.6

## Rounding Decimals

To round the decimal **24.6** to the nearest **whole number**, first **underline** the entire whole number. If the digit to the **right** of that number is 5 or higher, increase the whole number by one and leave off the decimal. If the digit to the **right** of that number is less than 5, keep the whole number the same and leave off the decimal.

24.6 Underline the 24. Look at the 6. Since 6 is greater than 5, change the 24 to 25 and leave off the decimal.

24.6 rounded to the nearest whole number is 25.

To round the decimal **8.31** to the nearest **tenth**, first underline the digit in the tenths place. Look at the digit to the right of that number (the hundredths place). If it is 5 or higher, increase the underlined digit by one and leave off the rest of the decimal. If it is less than 5, keep the underlined digit the same and leave off the rest of the decimal.

8.43 Underline the 4. Look at the 3. Since 3 is less than 5, keep the 4 the same and leave off the rest of the decimal.

8.43 rounded to the nearest tenth is 8.4.

**Round** each decimal to the **nearest whole number.**

1. 67.8 68
2. 16.05 16
3. 63.47 63
4. 37.68 38
5. 47.85 48
6. 123.4 123
7. 9.41 9
8. 9.76 10

**Round** each decimal to the **nearest tenth.**

9. 74.54 74.5
10. 82.17 82.2
11. 5.56 5.6
12. 32.73 32.7
13. 3.89 3.9
14. 5.64 5.6
15. 68.37 68.4
16. 6.86 6.9

36 Grade 4

## Math Review

You have done a terrific job. Now it is time to see how much you actually know!

**Tips for answering multiple choice questions:**

1. Always read the question carefully.
2. Get rid of any choices you know are definitely not right.
3. Even if you think that you have found the right answer, check all other choices to make sure they cannot be correct.

**CIRCLE the letter of the correct answer. Use a separate sheet of paper to work out each problem.**

1. Four million, sixteen thousand, two hundred thirty-six in **standard form** is:
   - A. 40,16, 236
   - B. 4,160,236
   - (C.) 4,016,236
   - D. 4,16,000,236

2. The **word name** for 27,008,054 is:
   - A. twenty-seven thousand, eight hundred fifty-four
   - (B.) twenty-seven million, eight thousand fifty-four
   - C. twenty-seven million, eighty-thousand
   - D. two million, seven hundred and eight thousand, fifty-four

3. In what place is the 0 in 43,078,234?
   - A. thousands
   - B. millions
   - (C.) hundred thousands
   - D. ten thousands

4. Which set of numbers is ordered from **greatest to least?**
   - A. 70,007 77,700 77,707
   - (B.) 77,777 70,700 70,007
   - C. 70,007 70,700 77,777
   - D. 77,777 70,007 70,700

5. 402,758 to the nearest **thousand** is:
   - A. 402,800
   - B. 502,758
   - C. 403,758
   - (D.) 403,000

6. A good estimate for 684 + 2,317 is:
   - A. 3,001
   - B. 2,700
   - (C.) 3,000
   - D. 3,700

*Smart Alec!* Mathematics 37

**7** $6,754 + 24,598 =$
A. 31,532
B. 30,352
(C.) 31,352
D. 31,252

**8** $706 - 89 =$
A. 627
B. 618
C. 613
(D.) 617

**9** A good estimate for $78 \times 534$ is:
A. 4,000
(B.) 40,000
C. 400,000
D. 41,652

**10** $653 \times 76 =$
A. 49,828
B. 8,489
(C.) 49,628
D. 48,628

**11** 85 divided by 9 is:
(A.) 9 R4
B. 9
C. 9 R5
D. 10

**12** If 702 is the dividend, and 6 is the divisor, what is the **quotient**?
A. 107
(B.) 117
C. 116 R6
D. 177

**13** The **product** of 504 and 8 is:
A. 512
(B.) 4,032
C. 4,112
D. 4,036

**14** $\frac{5}{8} + \frac{3}{8} =$
A. $\frac{8}{16}$
B. $\frac{1}{2}$
(C.) 1
D. $\frac{7}{8}$

**15** Which set of decimals is ordered from least to greatest?
A. 8.6 6.8 0.86 0.68
B. 8.6 6.8 0.86 0.68
C. 68 0.86 6.8 8.6
(D.) 0.68 0.86 6.8 8.6

**16** $6.8 - 2.59 =$
A. 4.29
B. 42.1
(C.) 4.21
D. 4.12